On Watch

For Nancy

Ab initio, ad infinitum

On Watch
Views from the Lighthouse

Christopher Spence

CASSELL

Cassell
Wellington House   215 Park Avenue South
125 Strand   New York
London   NY 10003
WC2R 0BB

First published 1996

British Library Cataloguing-in-Publication Data
A catalogue record for this book is available from the
British Library.

ISBN 0-304-33780-3 (paperback)

Designed by Information Design Workshop
Printed and bound in Great Britain by Biddles Ltd, of
Guildford and King's Lynn

Contents

PART 3

THERE'S A WORLD OUT THERE

PART 4

DEREK FRASER'S SONGS

Foreword by HRH The Princess of Wales

As a friend of London Lighthouse, which I have supported from its beginning and visited on many occasions, as well as Patron of the National AIDS Trust, I am particularly pleased to write the foreword to this book. *On Watch: Views from the Lighthouse* is a most readable, compelling, timely and hopeful book.

Written to mark the tenth anniversary of London Lighthouse, the inspiration for so many other initiatives in response to HIV and AIDS around the world, this short book is wide-ranging in its scope. Like my own involvement with the pandemic, through knowing people living with the virus, through my visits to many projects in London and throughout the United Kingdom as well as overseas, its focus is local, regional, national and international.

Christopher Spence begins with a moving account of the death of a friend, an experience which led him in 1986 to found London Lighthouse, overcoming fierce local opposition and raising the necessary funds for a purpose-built centre. He goes on to describe how hope and empowerment, in short supply the world over but the essential elements in any effective response to this terrible threat to public health, were reflected in the design of the project's beautiful building and of the integrated model of care developed there. His account of how, as the Lighthouse became a growing organisation, its philosophy was put into practice is one which is relevant for any organisation interested in what it means to work in human terms.

The author then looks beyond the Lighthouse, London and the United Kingdom. He identifies the pandemic as an issue of both health and human rights and, echoing the 1994 Paris Declaration, calls for partnership at every level of the global response. The book ends with tenth anniversary reflections on the Lighthouse vision, explored through the life and death of one member of staff, a description of the project as it is today and a lyrical final chapter.

Optimistic and inspirational in tone, the book does not avoid the challenges which face anyone taking leadership in the turbulent world of AIDS. As well as tackling opposition from the local community, for the author these included persuading decision-makers, dealing with conflicts within the project, handling attacks in the press and personal criticism, and struggling to resource the ever-expanding work. As the story of the Lighthouse and its influence unfolds, told from the author's unique perspective, philosophical, organisational, managerial, political, spiritual and ethical themes are woven into an extraordinary whole.

The pages of this book are *full* of hope, courage in the face of adversity and the possibility that, after all, dreams do come true! I wholeheartedly recommend this book to the countless thousands of people across the world who are committed to meeting this challenge of AIDS and who, as we all do from time to time, may need inspiration along the way.

Diana

January 1996

I was born for seeing
I am employed to watch
I am bound by my oath to this tower,
and I love the world.
I look into the distance
and see, as from nearby,
the moon and the stars,
the forest and the deer.
And in all of them I see
the eternal adornment;
and as the world delights me,
so I delight myself.
Oh, happy eyes,
whatever you have seen,
let it be as it may be,
it has been so beautiful!

J W von Goethe
Song from the Watch Tower
translated by David Luke

Preface: Why Write?

Our valley house in Oxfordshire is full of light. I sometimes think if there was nothing in the house, no fixtures, fittings, objects, pictures or clutter of any kind, all on its own the light would furnish it beautifully, forever rearranging itself in shafts and shadows, springing surprise after surprise every daylight hour.

Because it runs the length and height of the original part of the building, rather than because it is really all that long, we call our main room 'the long room'. Into this room light streams from a solid wall of glass looking onto the garden, and at each end from 20-foot-high windows angled to the beamed roof. It is a perfect setting for one of my favourite pastimes, arranging flowers. On special occasions I do them in an old soup tureen filled with a ball of chicken wire, standing it on a carved green pedestal at one end of the room. There the flowers dance and stretch and shimmer in the light, loudly announcing it's time to celebrate.

I imagine I learnt something of the art of flower arranging from watching my mother, though she never considered herself good at it, nor set out to pass on any principles to me. I only remember that she did it as she did everything, deftly and very fast, as if she knew exactly what to do, what length to cut the stems, what to put with what, how to create magic rather than a mess, massing the flowers in profusion, her finished arrangement perfectly in scale with the surroundings.

The ritual is always the same, familiar yet a bit unsettling, routine yet in its way mysterious. I go to market and buy whatever blooms are in season, augmenting them with foliage and anything else I can forage from the garden. I then soak it all in buckets of water overnight. Next day I approach the task of putting the arrangement together with little preconceived idea of what form it will take. I simply begin, first making a frame of the greenery or berries or blossom, next cutting the flowers, hammering their stems to make sure they can drink, finally placing them in the vase, supported by the chicken wire, apparently more or less at random.

Invariably, at a certain point along the way, the arrangement takes on its own momentum, a coherence of shape and pattern and size and combination of colours emerging, almost always declaring itself finished just at the point when there are no more flowers. Without fail, having lost track of time and ankle-deep in clippings, for me, the arranger, the pleasure is intense.

In its way my other favourite pastime, writing, is a bit like flower arranging. At least as far as this book is concerned, since I know I am writing in the first place for pleasure, for my own pleasure and I hope other people's too. It may seem odd, frivolous and irreverent even, to be setting out unashamedly to get and give pleasure in writing a book about HIV and AIDS, or at least about one small part of the global response, London Lighthouse.

But then, why not? After ten extraordinary years, years spent as it were at market, in the garden, in the woods and fields and hedgerows, I find myself surrounded by buckets crammed with such a profusion of foliage and flowers and berries of every season and variety, all more or less agitating, it seems to me, to be arranged as something lovely. And if I approach my task faithful to the values which have brought Lighthouse safely to this point, then I must be personal, start with myself, begin without knowing quite what will result, trusting the project is worth the effort, above all not getting in the way.

Recently there was a reception at the Lighthouse for representatives of what are called 'linking' organisations in developing countries. Working through the International HIV/AIDS Alliance, these organisations link donors in the west with AIDS projects on the ground. During the evening Kamanee Hapugalle, from an organisation called Alliance Lanka, made a wonderful speech. She said she had been so moved by her visit to the Lighthouse that she wanted to leave us a gift. Holding up a small, brilliant-bright carved elephant she said she wanted everyone present to touch it, and afterwards to place it in the spot where a candle burns when someone at the Lighthouse dies. 'It is to remind you that in Sri Lanka we do not forget you, we will always be thinking of you.'

This book is for Kamanee Hapugalle, a gift in return. It is also for Noerine Kaleeba of TASO, Uganda, now based at UNAIDS in Geneva, who sat in the garden at the Lighthouse and said I must write it; and for

Radium Bhattacharya of Gujarat AIDS Prevention in Ahmedabad, whom, with my colleague Richard Foord, I shall be visiting in India before long. It's for Ian McKnight and my friends at Jamaica AIDS Support; and for John Campbell of the UK Coalition of People Living with HIV and AIDS, currently in Ibiza shaking off the threat of multi drug-resistant tuberculosis.

It's for Ernst Meibeck, in the hope that there's still time for him to read it, who last time we spoke was in a hospital bed still working away on the lighthouse of his dreams, the Hamburg 'Leuchtfeuer'. It's for Julio Tarrago da Silveira of Alternativa Positiva in Lisbon, who writes to me about his struggles almost every month, battering me with questions and taking no notice of my answers. And it's for Ivan Battle, who devoted his time with the virus to building a musical academy in North Carolina along the same lines as the Lighthouse, and who, before he died in 1995, wrote us a song in celebration, 'Bring Me Home'.

The book is for them and for the hundreds and thousands of people all over the world who have committed themselves to meeting this challenge in one way or another, or who will one day do so. And, though they won't read it, it's for everyone who has died along the way, those 'stars in your multitude, scarce to be counted, filling the darkness with order and light'.

To celebrate our tenth anniversary and written with love, it's a birthday book for the Lighthouse, wishing it many good years to come. And for anyone interested in how dreams come true, how they encourage hope and stir the human spirit, and how they may even change the world in some small way, it's for you too.

The purpose of the book is not really to educate or inform or explain, nothing as lofty as that, though I'll be glad if it sheds a little light here and there. Nor is it a 'how to' book, a horrible thought. (They never have the answer to the thing I *really* need to know - it's the same with computer manuals.) Nor is it to record everything that happened fully and objectively. I'm too close and, if warranted, that's a task for historians. I have a story to tell, but the point of the story is the point, not the story. When people are part of the point, they appear in the story. When they don't, or you don't, it's not that they, or you, aren't part of the story, just not on that page at that point, that's all.

The first part of the book deals with the genesis of Lighthouse and how it came to pass. The next describes how we've tried to put the philosophy to work. The third part looks out, beyond Lighthouse itself to the wider world of the pandemic. Next comes Derek Fraser's Songs, some anniversary reflections on the Lighthouse vision. The final two chapters celebrate Lighthouse and the writing of the book itself. Some bits are brand new, others have appeared before in articles or speeches, now reshaped for readability and balance. Except where attributed otherwise, it's all my own work. That means I must take responsibility and so I do.

In her deliciously witty and wise book on writing, *Bird by Bird*, Anne Lamott addresses the question, why write?

> *Against all odds, you have put it down on paper, so that it won't be lost. And who knows? Maybe what you've written will help others, will be a small part of the solution. You don't even have to know how or in what way, but if you are writing the clearest, truest words you can find and doing the best you can to understand and communicate, this will shine on paper like its own little lighthouse. Lighthouses don't go running all over an island looking for boats to save; they just stand there shining.*

> *Then I look into my students' faces, and they look solemnly back at me.*

> *'So why does our writing matter, again?' they ask.*

> *Because of the spirit, I say. Because of the heart. Writing and reading decrease our sense of isolation. They deepen and widen and expand our sense of life: they feed the soul. When writers make us shake our heads at the exactness of their prose and their truths, and even make us laugh about ourselves or life, our buoyancy is restored. We are given a shot at dancing with, or at least clapping along with, the absurdity of life, instead of being squashed by it over and over again. It's like singing on a boat during a terrible storm at sea. You can't stop the raging storm, but singing can change the hearts and spirits of the people who are together on that ship.*

Yes. All that.

And I write too for the sheer joy of it, the joy of arranging flowers in a vase. Flowers to remind us of life, to nourish hope and revive spirits, to encourage, inspire, or simply to give a little pleasure.

That's why.

Acknowledgements

There are many people to thank for their help in writing this book.

I am deeply grateful to Her Royal Highness The Princess of Wales for generously writing the foreword as well as for being a most constant friend to the issue of HIV/AIDS, to the Lighthouse and to me.

Andrew Henderson and his colleagues on the Lighthouse Council of Management kindly granted me leave of absence to write the book. Susie Parsons, our Executive Director, cheerfully picked up the extra work, backing the project with characteristic enthusiasm and encouragement. She sent a card of bright red poppies to greet me at the start of my writing retreat and was first to read and comment on the earliest draft. Together with my personal assistant, Jenny Fowler, Susie also saw to it that I wasn't disturbed more than absolutely necessary.

Matthew Davis, Head of Communications at Lighthouse, steered the manuscript through its various stages, working on the design with Helen Martins and Rosie Leyden of Wordworks, Bill Mayblin of Information Design Workshop and Steve Cook, my publisher at Cassell. As far as I know, there was never a cross word and I thank them all for their commitment to producing a beautiful book and for making my part such a pleasure. Helen Martins, until her move to Wordworks our Publications Officer at Lighthouse, edited much of the material in its original form as well as this manuscript. No writer could wish for a more thorough, validating and attentive editor. Gilly Glyn was, as always, a source of unconditional support from start to finish and I cannot thank her enough.

The Dean of Westminster, The Very Reverend Michael Mayne, another generous, long-term ally, inspired me with his book, *This Sunrise of Wonder - Letters for the Journey*, to write mine my way. There, among many other treasures, I discovered the Goethe poem 'Song from the Watch Tower'. There too I rediscovered what Dennis Potter said about dying in that enthralling conversation with Melvyn Bragg shown on Channel 4 shortly before his death in 1994.

I thank my friend and colleague Lisa Power for extracts from 'Collaboration of Service NGOs in a Market Environment', a paper presented at the Second BioPsychoSocial Aspects of AIDS Conference in Brighton in July 1994; and Dr Jonathan Mann for the quotations from 'AIDS in 1994: The Personal and Global Challenge of Renewal', his speech at the Tenth International Conference on AIDS in Yokohama, Japan.

I am grateful to the following companies and individuals for granting permission for the use of copyright material:

PAGE XII
'Song from the Watch Tower' by J W von Goethe, translated by David Luke, in *This Sunrise of Wonder - Letters for the Journey by Michael Mayne,* reproduced by permission of HarperCollins Publishers Ltd.

PREFACE
Lines from 'Stars' from *Les Misérables*, a musical by Alain Boublil and Claude-Michel Schönberg, lyrics by Herbert Kretzmer.

CHAPTER 1
Lines from 'Breaths', poem by Birago Diop, adapted and set to music by Ysaye M Barnwell © 1980, recorded by Sweet Honey in the Rock. Reproduced by kind permission of Westbury Music Ltd/Barnwell's Notes.

CHAPTER 9
Faber and Faber Ltd for an extract from 'Little Gidding' by T S Eliot in the *Four Quartets.*

CHAPTER 19
Verses from *The Prophet* by Kahlil Gibran. Copyright 1923 by Kahlil Gibran and renewed 1951 by Administrators CTA of Kahlil Gibran Estate and Mary G Gibran. Reprinted by permission of Alfred A Knopf Inc.

CHAPTER 20
Extract from an interview with Dennis Potter by Melvyn Bragg Channel 4 1994 by permission from Richard Scott Simon Ltd part of Sheil Land Associates. Quotation by Nigel Sheldrick from *Embracing the Chaos - Theological Responses to AIDS*, edited by James Woodward, 1990, used by permission of the publisher SPCK.

CHAPTER 22
Lines from 'Glad to be Gay' by Tom Robinson. Used by kind permission of Tom Robinson (Leosong).

CHAPTER 26
Definition of 'family', from the *Concise Oxford Dictionary*, 8th edition, 1990, by permission of Oxford University Press.

CHAPTER 30
Nancy Kline for extracts from *Women and Power: How Far Can We Go?*

PART 4 INTRODUCTION
'The Truly Great' from *Collected Poems 1928-1985* by Stephen Spender.
Copyright © 1986 by Stephen Spender. Published by Faber and Faber Ltd.
Reprinted by permission of Faber and Faber Ltd and Random House Inc.

CHAPTER 31
Lines from 'Healing Hands' by Elton John. Reproduced by permission of the
Elton John AIDS Foundation and Happenstance Ltd 1989.

CHAPTER 32
Lines from '(There is) No Greater Love', music by Isham Jones and words
by Marty Symes. © 1936, Music Sales Co, USA. Reproduced by permission
of Keith Prowse Music Pub Co Ltd/EMI Music Publishing Ltd, London
WC2H 0EA.

CHAPTER 33
Definition of 'vision', from the *Concise Oxford Dictionary*, 8th edition, 1990, by
permission of Oxford University Press.
Lines from 'We Have All the Time in the World', music by John Barry and
words by Hal David. © 1969 EMI United Partnership Ltd (worldwide print
rights controlled by Warner Bros Publications Inc/IMP Ltd.

CHAPTER 34
Jimmy Somerville for lines from 'For a Friend'.

CHAPTER 37
Extract from W B Yeats 'Earth, Fire and Water', from *The Celtic Twilight*, and
extract from W B Yeats 'Where My Books Go', from *The Oxford Book of
English Verse 1250-1900*, both reproduced by kind permission of A P Watt
Ltd on behalf of Anne and Michael Yeats.

Every effort has been made to trace copyright owners and I
apologise to anyone whose rights have inadvertently been
unacknowledged. This will of course be corrected in any reprint.

Finally I thank my wife Nancy, a writer herself, who helped me
every step of the way. Although hard at work on a book herself, she was
always ready to hear every piece, not once but twice or more, excitement
bubbling at the prospect of another instalment. Understanding that the
book must shape itself and maintaining a ten to one ratio of appreciation
to criticism, she never held back from saying exactly what she thought.
The quality of her thinking is extraordinary and the book, like the
Lighthouse itself, would probably never have happened without her.

Christopher Spence
London Lighthouse
June 1996

Note on Author

Born in West Sussex in 1944, Christopher Spence began his working life in the voluntary sector, becoming Director of Task Force in London in 1969. This was followed by six years as Private Secretary to the Speaker of the House of Commons, Selwyn Lloyd. For the next decade he worked as a freelance counsellor, trainer, writer and consultant to organisations in the health and social services, the churches, education and the youth service, as well as in industry and commerce, both in the United Kingdom and abroad.

A particular interest in death, dying, bereavement, loss and separation, and their centrality in the wider context of social change, led him in 1981 to set up Lifestory, a counselling and training centre in west London. Here by the mid-1980s HIV and AIDS had become the major focus of his work. In 1986 he founded London Lighthouse, the internationally-acclaimed residential and support centre for men and women affected by HIV and AIDS which is the subject of this book.

He is the author of *A Homecoming and the Harvest* (winner of the 1980 Oxford Institute of Religion and Medicine Essay Prize), *AIDS: Time to Reclaim our Power* and, with Nancy Kline, of *At Least a Hundred Principles of Love*. Presenting a personal but universally applicable view of love as a vehicle to establish permanent political and social change, these principles underpin the radical philosophy of the Lighthouse.

Christopher Spence is founding Chair of the Pan London HIV/AIDS Providers Consortium. He was awarded the MBE in 1992. He is married to the writer and consultant Nancy Kline and they live in Oxfordshire.

Part 1

When dreams come true

Until you are committed, there is hesitancy, the chance to draw back, always ineffectiveness.

Concerning all acts of initiative (and creation) there is one elementary truth, the ignorance of which kills countless ideas and endless plans; that the moment you definitely commit yourself, then providence moves too. All sorts of things occur to help you that would never have otherwise occurred.

A whole stream of events issues from the decision, raising in your favour all manner of unforeseen incidents and meetings and material assistance, which you could not have dreamed would come your way.

Whatever you can do or dream you can - begin it.

Boldness has genius, power and magic in it.

J W von Goethe

Chapter 1
Frank

I first met Frank Wilson in Dublin where he was living with his partner Albert Ogle, an Anglican priest. Albert had invited me to lead a gay liberation workshop at a reconciliation centre in the Wicklow mountains just outside Dublin. Frank was welcoming and friendly enough, but shy and cautious about the proposed workshop in which he was apparently not intending to participate himself. As if to prove him right, later there were reprisals and a parish 'outing'. Albert was duly punished for his temerity, losing both his job and the house that went with it. Gay refugees, together they came to live in London.

One day in March 1985, several years later, now on his own, having parted from Albert who was living in Los Angeles, Frank telephoned me saying he needed help and wanted to come and see me. Calling in that evening on his way home from work, he walked into my study, sat down and baldly said, 'I've got AIDS, I'm going to die and I want your support.'

AIDS. This was *the* issue which, like so many people I knew, especially those living in gay relationships as I then was, I had not wanted to face, much less take on as my own. At defining moments like this you *know*, you know what is being asked of you, you know what lies ahead; but at the same time you don't know *what* you know. I knew without question that I would give Frank all the support I possibly could; I think I also knew that this would lead me to something important I had been avoiding; beyond that I knew nothing. I was scared.

He told me that lying on the beach in Greece the summer before, he had felt an unfamiliar weight on his chest. Through the autumn he began to feel very unwell, steadily losing weight and developing a nasty bout of thrush. Then, blazoned across the tabloid press, he read of the death from AIDS of a friend with whom he had been sexual. Putting two and two together he guessed what was wrong. That night he said to me,

'Christopher, I really don't want to spin things out. I know it's hopeless.' Shortly after this Frank went into hospital for treatment to boost his immune system and there, found to have Kaposi's Sarcoma, an AIDS diagnosis was confirmed. Before long he developed pneumonia and, after a battle to save his life during which he was put on a ventilator in intensive care, a most horrible experience, he died on 1 May.

Of course these bare facts do not tell the whole story. Thirty-three years old and an accountant by trade, Frank was modest, thoughtful, generous, a man of integrity and quiet wit. He grew up in a small town in the Lake District where his father was a baker and his mother a cleaner in a boarding school. When Frank was 16 his mother was killed, a loss from which he never really recovered. He told me that from then on there was always a part of him which wanted to die, to be with his mother again.

As a working-class gay man, there was another part of Frank which had low expectations of life. He had difficulty in recognising himself or his needs as in any way important; he battled with feelings of worthlessness and had little sense of his own goodness. None of this put him in a strong position when AIDS came his way.

It was rather like watching a man fight with his hands tied behind his back. Frank's handcuffs were that chronic sense of *wanting* to die, heartbroken at the loss of his mother, and of *deserving* to die, since deep down he felt no good. This double-bind left him struggling to tackle the complement of challenges which now filled his days: coming to terms with a life-threatening diagnosis, resisting infection, coping with terror in almost every face he saw, adjusting to isolation and barrier nursing, challenging the ways in which his diagnosis, in combination with his homosexuality, triggered the most bizarre behaviour in others, and assuming control of his life as a sick person, soon likely to die.

It was inspiring to me that in the face of such odds, though he lost the battle against AIDS, Frank did bravely fight and win, for the first time perhaps, the battle to be fully himself and in charge of his life before he died. He grieved for the mother he expected shortly to rejoin. He made an effort to raise his self-esteem and to combat his sense of worthlessness. He reached powerfully for those around him, cheerfully disregarding their discomfort about AIDS and overlooking their homophobia.

Assertively, but without any encouragement to do so, he persisted in asking his doctors for information. He cried when he needed to, at least until alarmed hospital staff prescribed tranquillisers which numbed his emotions altogether. He set right his relationships, becoming fierce, honest and expressive with his family and friends as never before. He faced up to the fact that he was dying with courage and equanimity and, with characteristic precision, was ready to depart just when he had accomplished everything he needed to do first. Laboriously using his speaking board, tapping out the words letter by letter, he told me that the battle on the ventilator in intensive care was only a vain attempt on the part of well-intentioned doctors to keep him alive past the point when he had decided it was time to die, what he termed his sell-by date.

I had the great joy and good fortune to stay close to Frank throughout his illness and death. As his condition deteriorated, especially after he was transferred to intensive care, he wanted someone with him as much of the time as possible, day and night. His sister Patsy, his only sibling, came to visit as did other friends. Albert came from Los Angeles to say his goodbyes, although by now Frank was only able to communicate through the speaking board: 'I love you and I always will' he tapped.

Now every working day, very early in the morning, I drive past that hospital where Frank died. Every day I look, remember and feel thankful for those days and nights and for his many parting gifts, not least the profoundly changed course of my life. Thanks to Frank I made my reluctant acquaintance with AIDS, this lethal brew. I saw sensible, well-meaning professionals too terrified to think, altogether excluding Frank from the decision-making process. I came up against the rigidities of a health care system which provides service stations rather than dignified last ports of call. I watched the dehumanising, degrading effects of unnecessary barrier nursing, with all its disconnecting paraphernalia, and the lack of real attention to the person at the centre of things, Frank.

I saw the scars of unresolved grief and the way they weaken the will to live. I observed how the internalised effects of oppression, in Frank's case as a working-class gay man, impose limiting assumptions of powerlessness, ravaging the human spirit to survive and thrive. Outraged, I witnessed at first hand what, often with the best intentions, can happen to people in our medicalised, death-denying, oppressive society. Why, I wondered, why on earth should anyone ever have to die like this, combating homophobia, lying strapped to a ventilator on a hospital trolley in a bleak, clinical, intensive care unit, attended only by faceless people in masks and gowns and gloves? Surely, surely there must be a better way than this?

And in answer to the question came the germ of an idea.

Surrounding the fountain in our beautiful garden behind the Lighthouse is a water garden filled with plants and stones which is dedicated to Frank. A small, suitably modest plaque has a quotation from a song recorded by Sweet Honey in the Rock, 'Breaths'. It reads:

IN MEMORY

FRANK WILSON

1953 -1985

THOSE WHO HAVE DIED HAVE NEVER NEVER LEFT
THE DEAD HAVE A PACT WITH THE LIVING
THEY ARE IN THE WOMAN'S BREAST
THEY ARE IN THE WAILING CHILD
THEY ARE WITH US IN THE HOME
THEY ARE WITH US IN THE CROWD
THE DEAD HAVE A PACT WITH THE LIVING

Frank would have liked that. He would also have been astonished at what has come to pass.

Chapter 2
Listen Well

The day Frank died, 1 May, Labour Day, is also the birthday of Nancy Kline, to whom I am now married. At that time our love affair was nearly two years old, she was living in the United States and we had developed the expensive habit of talking on the telephone every day. Sad and drained by the death-bed vigil, I called to wish her happy birthday and to tell her that Frank had died. I also told her I had decided to do whatever I could to make sure that no-one should ever again have to die as Frank had done. A simple decision, but how was I to get started?

A few days later I was telephoned by someone I had never met, Jonathan Grimshaw. He told me that, together with others, he had started a group called Body Positive. They wanted to train support group leaders, and he had been given my name as someone with relevant skills. We agreed to meet with others at an address in Earls Court to talk things over. It turned out to be a flat with no furniture except a dentist's chair in the middle of the room. I sat in the dentist's chair and after listening to what everyone had to say, I agreed to lead a support group.

Based on the co-counselling model, the formula was simple but effective. People took turns to be listened to and to listen, in pairs and in the group. Basic counselling skills were taught, stories told, experience shared, tears shed, fear and rage vented, goals set, support given and received.

Before long people were reporting positive changes in their lives. And very soon more and more people were getting in touch, asking to join a group. As numbers grew we began to get a picture of the hostility of the social climate in which people were having to deal with an HIV-positive diagnosis, of the degree of ignorance, prejudice, misinformation, harassment and discrimination routinely encountered, and of the difficulty for some in accessing health and social care.

It was not yet clear what or how or when, but already we were talking about the need for a radical alternative, an AIDS-specific place of safety where people could look with confidence, knowing that they would be treated with respect and that their needs, as defined by them, would be well met.

But we were also learning about empowerment. One early recruit, Graham Gardner, with only about a year left to live, went to the heart of it when he said, 'I realise that this diagnosis of AIDS presents me with a choice: the choice either to be a hopeless victim, or to make my life right now what it always ought to have been.' This notion of choice is fundamental in the philosophy which evolved: the choice to see HIV/AIDS as a grim crisis for humanity, or instead to see it as an opportunity, individually and collectively, to move forward. Would HIV merely reinforce people's powerlessness, despair, hopelessness, isolation and fear of being all they can be, or could it, in fact, become a springboard for personal and social change? It seemed to me that one option was a good deal more interesting than the other.

Early in 1986 I wrote a book, *AIDS: Time to Reclaim our Power*. It is addressed particularly to gay men, who were the majority of those involved in the network at that time, though its message is universal and it enjoyed a wider readership. Building on an earlier writing collaboration with Nancy Kline, *At Least a Hundred Principles of Love*, it sets out to map this terrain we had been exploring in support groups and workshops, which only later we came to call empowerment.

The framework is simple and falls into three parts: taking care of ourselves; putting love at the centre of our lives; and living without limits. Focusing on these three interlocking circles, the book is divided into 32 short chapters, signposting what adopting a positive perspective on HIV/AIDS might mean in practice. The book proceeds from the thesis that the first, powerful act of self-love is the decision to exist, to be born, to engage with life - a decision probably taken in the womb. If we adopt this assumption, then why not also assume we can choose to reach back across all the subsequent defeats to the high expectations we arrived with, to reconnect with that first decision, to live?

At the same time, paradoxically, we can come to a good understanding of death, to see dying as something which in due course we shall *do* (with or without AIDS), our destiny, the healthy conclusion to life. Put these two together and we have a baseline for living well in the present; for taking charge of our health, looking after our bodies, eating and exercising well, balancing activity and rest, giving up self-abuse in all its forms, including our addictions, and paying attention to our emotional well-being.

Because isolation is potentially an even bigger enemy than the virus itself - it is hard to be positive and powerful in the face of a life-threatening diagnosis if you are on your own - the second part of our book deals with relationships, in the first place our relationships with ourselves. As Frank's story shows, the internalised effects of oppression often make this very challenging for gay men. But supposing we begin to treat ourselves as well as we treat those we love most, turning unconditional love in as well as out, appreciating ourselves as the marvels we are? Isn't this the place from which to challenge isolation, to assume we are loved, to restore family ties, to surround ourselves with intimacy, friendship and intelligent support, to make sure that everything about our lives and environment reflects this level of love for ourselves?

The third part of the book explores what flows from the choice to assume our goodness and significance, the meaning and purpose of our lives, our innate leadership. Joy, it suggests, is the soundest motivation for action; our own thinking, based in what we find out for ourselves, the safest place to put our trust. If we really set aside the limiting assumptions of powerlessness both in the goals we set and in the action we take to fulfil them, we can expect change and upheaval along the way. Don't believe we can't have everything; we can.

> Stay true to the voice within. This voice is our smartest, unhurt self who knows at every juncture what is best to do and does not ever bend to fear. If we listen well this is the voice we can trust. This is the voice which beckons us at birth and bids us be unafraid of death. It is the voice which informs our finest thinking, prompts our boldest decisions, adds beauty, lustre, and power to our actions. It is the voice which strengthens and softens our loving. It is the tireless champion of our health and vigour. This is the voice which holds us safe in the eye of the storm when it rages round our head. It is the voice of our good conscience, in tune with the things of the spirit, with wisdom, with nature, with God.

> This is the voice which can be counted on to tell the truth when lies assail us. It will always speak of what is right and good and lovely. It calls us to laugh and to play. It sings our best songs. It encourages creation. It is never distracted or confused, or too busy to whisper reminders of our goodness and humanity. It will never pretend. This voice believes in neither fate nor coincidence. It confirms the rightness of our right choices. It is familiar with our place in the scheme of things. It celebrates our dreams. It knows us, and all that is dear to us, well. It is the guide we can trust.

This was a powerful message, flying in the face of the prevailing doom and gloom and so much hysteria about HIV/AIDS in the press. What had begun as an informal network of essentially local support grew and grew. Soon we were offering residential workshops in retreat centres to more than a hundred people at a time: people living with the virus, family and friends, pastors, health and social care professionals, workers in the emerging HIV/AIDS sector, a growing army of supporters and even, in the course of time, funders.

Soon 'Life, Death and the Challenge of AIDS' went international with workshops taking place in Ireland, Sweden, France, the Netherlands, Switzerland and the United States of America. Later Nancy Kline and I developed a parallel workshop, 'Love, Power and the Immune System' which focused on the connection between lifestyle, particularly self-esteem and intimacy, and the capacity of the immune system to do its work well.

Things were moving very fast.

Chapter 3
Out of the Sky

People are always asking me how the project came to be called Lighthouse. Try as I might I have never succeeded in persuading anyone to claim the credit.

I had convened a small group to try to get that germ of an idea to sprout. There were six of us: Andrew Henderson, Director of Social Services in the area where he and I had been living together for many years, the Royal Borough of Kensington & Chelsea; John Shine, a nurse counsellor at St Stephen's Hospital (later rebuilt as the Chelsea & Westminster), one of the main local HIV/AIDS treatment centres; Debbie Evans, a manager in the same hospital; Peter Randall, co-founder with Jonathan Grimshaw of Body Positive; John Fitzpatrick, Deputy Chief Executive of the Terrence Higgins Trust; and myself.

Several years earlier, as part of my work for a counselling diploma in which my special subject had been death, dying and bereavement, I had worked with the help of Andrew Henderson, Donald Eadie, a local Methodist minister and others, to develop a blueprint for an imaginary community-based project, which I had called The Notting Hill Centre for Life and Death. My idea had been to try and blur the boundaries between health and social care by combining in one project supported housing, domiciliary care, a social centre where people could access a range of services on a drop-in basis, including bereavement counselling, and a residential facility offering respite and terminal care.

At that stage Andrew and I were living in a small flat at the top of Ladbroke Grove. I would often bicycle to the Ecumenical Church in Lancaster Road, where there were rooms I hired for my classes and workshops. It seemed to me that Lancaster Road, on the Notting Hill Carnival route, was an important axis. Running east to west across Portobello Road and Ladbroke Grove, it was a natural crossing point for the very diverse population of north Kensington.

It was here, in my mind's eye at least, that I sited my project. But this was all long before HIV and AIDS arrived and I suppose it was an idea before its time. There was no context for taking it beyond the drawing board.

At least not then.

But in 1981 Andrew and I took one significant step when we moved into a large house on Lancaster Road. It had a roomy basement, an ideal home for Lifestory, the counselling and training centre we set up to focus on loss and bereavement. Until we grew out of it, it was here that we developed the support network which was to become London Lighthouse. With french windows into the garden and its own kitchen, it was a cosy, womb-like place full of bean bags and huge cushions. People got very attached to it, finding it a great wrench to leave when the time came.

But there was uncanny resonance between that earlier idea, now tucked between the covers of my diploma portfolio, gathering dust, and the radical alternative we wanted for people living with the virus. One afternoon a few members of the group were sitting round the kitchen table in our house upstairs drinking tea and talking, talking, talking about this dream-without-a-name. It will be a place of safety, domestic not institutional, offering an 'integrated' continuum of care enabling people to live and die well. It will offer a range of services at any point between diagnosis with HIV and death from AIDS so that with minimal formality people can move from one to another as circumstances change, always central in decisions about their care. Its message will be hope and empowerment. It will challenge prejudice, oppression and the denial of death. It will involve people living with the virus in the design and delivery of services and in running the project itself. Above all it will be a place where people will be well-treated, with love, respect and real attention.

We begin playing with images. Shining a light, leading the way, showing the world what's possible. Guiding people safely home - 'home to what?', someone asks - 'to themselves, to one another, to the edge, or end, of life itself.' A beacon for change. A strong and sturdy edifice in stormy seas ... of course, that's it, a lighthouse.

Right out of the sky, this beautiful image arrives in our midst. It is perfect. Another defining moment.

At that stage, none of us was envisaging starting such a project ourselves. That would be far too big an undertaking and besides weren't we all much too committed elsewhere? No, surely this was an idea to be carried forward in the public sector, by the health service or by the local authority?

So then began a weary round of meetings with officialdom. In the main people were very friendly and receptive. 'Yes,' they would say, 'HIV prevalence is significant and set to rise, we know there is a crisis looming and it's one we haven't planned for adequately. Your Lighthouse idea sounds excellent. It makes a lot of sense.' 'And how would it be developed by health/housing/social services?', I would ask. Invariably the reply was disappointing. As we were picturing it, Lighthouse did not fit neatly into any of these three distinct frameworks for statutory provision. That was the point. It broke new ground and there was no familiar formula to fall back on. People just couldn't quite hear what was being described.

So it wasn't very long before I came to the conclusion that at all costs the project must not be put into the hands of the statutory sector. If that was to happen, I could see it taking years and years to develop and, in the end, it not being the radical alternative we knew was needed now.

Nancy was here on a visit. Driving together down Ladbroke Grove one evening I said to her, 'I think I am going to have to start this project myself.' Sniffing scents of upheaval in the *modus vivendi* we had worked out against the odds, the threat to our bimonthly trips across the Atlantic and our times away together writing, her heart sank. At the same time, she knew this project was right - and right for me - and that therefore it would be good for our relationship.

'Yes,' she said quietly, 'I think so too.'

Chapter 4
That's Our Building

'I think we're going about this the wrong way,' I said to the group next time we met. 'There hasn't been anything quite like Lighthouse before and people just can't get it. I think we must find a building, start the work and demonstrate what we're talking about.'

Dead silence. Everyone seemed paralysed, hopeless, overwhelmed at the magnitude of the task. Soon the air was thick with 'yes, but ...'. Obstacles began piling up in an ugly heap, making it hard to think. At that moment we weren't a particularly empowered group of people and we couldn't see beyond the real difficulties, like, for example, lack of money. So the meeting broke up and everyone left, rather discouraged. Where could we go from here?

Afterwards I was looking out of the bay window in my study in a reverie. 'Where would we begin to look for a building of the size we need,' I asked myself, 'when all we have is a good idea and £700 in the bank?' Suddenly the derelict school across the street swam into focus. Without any hesitation and with unaccountable certainty the thought came into my mind, '*That's* our building.'

It seems odd to admit, since I had by now lived opposite that school for more than five years, that I had never really noticed it before. Now, eyeing it closely for the first time, I could see that it was completely unsuitable for Lighthouse. Enclosed by a forbidding high wall, it was institutional, ugly, linear, derelict and in every way the antithesis of what we had been imagining. But that thought just wouldn't go away. 'I've found the building,' I told people. 'Where?' they asked. 'There,' I would say, pointing at the school. 'But Christopher,' would come the appalled reply, 'that's a horrible, depressing dump of a place, we couldn't possibly put the Lighthouse there!'

Andrew was supportive. He offered to enquire at the Town Hall who owned the building although, in the event, no-one there seemed to know. It had formerly been the Solomon Wolfson Jewish School, which seven years earlier had been relocated nearer to where the Jewish community it served was now living. Since then it had been derelict and we couldn't find anyone who knew the identity of the present owners. We finally rang the Town Hall again and asked whether rates were paid and, if so, to whom they sent the bill. 'To the building', we were told.

I decided the only thing to do was write a letter. 'To whom it may concern,' it said, 'please contact me as a matter of urgency concerning this building.' But there was nowhere obvious to deliver it. The gates were chained and the two other entrances, one marked BOYS and the other GIRLS, were bricked up. So, hoping for the best, I shoved it through a hole in the wall and went off to lead a workshop in Sweden. When I returned there was a courteous, if puzzled, reply from the Cultural Attaché at the Spanish Embassy in London, thanking me for my letter and asking the nature of my enquiry. Apparently the Spanish government had bought the school with the intention of turning it into a community centre for Spanish-speaking people in west London. That idea had not got off the ground and now, since there was concern about its security and the threat of vandals or squatters, it might well be that the government in Madrid would consider selling the freehold. So far so good. I asked if I could see the building. Obligingly, the Cultural Attaché came himself to show me round.

It would be hard to imagine a more depressing experience. If anything it was worse inside than it looked from the outside, dark, damp, bare and falling to pieces. I remember a sodden piano standing forlornly in a corridor tilting on three castors. Incongruously, in the old synagogue at the back there were piles of Catholic missals, all in Spanish, crucifixes, candlesticks and all sorts of ecclesiastical debris.

'What kind of figure do you think the government has in mind?' I asked. I was told that offers in the region of £400,000 might be considered favourably. 'Well, we are definitely interested,' I said, smiling to myself at the thought of our £700 in the bank, a gift from Graham Gardner. Then Andrew suggested that we contact an old friend of ours, Christopher Gibbs, a near neighbour in Oxfordshire where we spent our weekends. He was a trustee of the John Paul Getty Junior Charitable Trust. Earlier he had told Andrew that he hoped the Trust might make some contribution to AIDS and if we had concrete ideas to get in touch. We went over to see Christopher one evening and told him what we had in mind. He was impressed. 'This needs to be done,' he said, 'And I think you are the boys to do it.' If we would write a proposal, he would put the matter to his fellow trustees when next they met later that week.

Frantically we worked to pull together as much data as we could about HIV prevalence in west London and to put on paper our ideas for the Lighthouse. A few days later the Getty trustees sent a message to say that they were interested in our proposal and would like to see the building we were proposing to buy.

Given the state of the building and the frankly sketchy ideas we had about what we were going to do with it, this was rather an alarming prospect. Nevertheless, the Cultural Attaché agreed to this further visit and came to let us in. Wearing bowler hats and carrying black umbrellas, the Getty trustees duly arrived by taxi and we took them on a guided tour, in reality only flying by the seat of our pants, but doing our best to give a credible explanation of how the building could be adapted to serve the needs of the Lighthouse.

They said almost nothing, at least until we got to the far end of the top floor, into what must have been the school kitchen. Along one wall was a huge old gas range, probably dating from 1929 when the school was built. One of the trustees stood in front of it for a long time, contemplating. Finally he turned to the others and said, 'You know, I think with wire wool and elbow grease, this could be buffed up and brought back into commission.'

There and then they said this was an exciting concept and they would support us; they would ensure that we acquired the building. 'Then you won't have that to worry about and you can get on and develop the project.' They were as good as their word even though, once the Spanish government got wind that John Paul Getty was interested in buying the old school, we were locked into a Dutch auction and the price went up and up and up.

Looking back, I think this was the most anxious period of all. Would we or wouldn't we get this building? Supposing we lost it and had to go back to square one? I remember lying in my bath one day fretting, going over and over things in my mind, torturing myself with nightmare 'what if?' scenarios. Then suddenly, for no apparent reason, I decided that worrying was stupid, a complete waste of energy. Either this project was meant to be in this building, in which case we would get it, or it wasn't, in which case we wouldn't and something else would turn up. Then and there I decided to quit worrying and I've hardly ever worried since.

Finally, on 5 August 1986, we acquired the freehold of the former Solomon Wolfson Jewish School for £800,000: £700,000 was a two-year interest-free loan and £50,000 an outright gift from the Getty Trust;

£50,000 was a matching gift from the Delamere Trust, a private charitable trust of which Andrew is a trustee. On that same historic day the project became a legal entity. The Charity Commissioners granted us charitable status and we were registered at Companies House as a non-profit-distributing company. Now we not only had our good idea, rather better formulated than before, we had at last taken formal shape as an organisation (albeit one with no staff or resources of any kind) and we were the proud owners of a totally derelict building. And, remember, we still had £700 in the bank.

So London Lighthouse was born. Everything was possible now. Little did we know that trouble was brewing, right around the corner.

Chapter 5
Opposition

Now the building was ours, we wanted to lodge a planning application quickly. We commissioned Andrew Cowser, a local architect who had been involved in the support network, to produce some preliminary drawings. Then we applied to the Royal Borough of Kensington & Chelsea, our local authority, for permission to convert the former Solomon Wolfson Jewish School into a residential and support centre for people affected by HIV and AIDS. I really didn't expect any difficulty, at least not from the local community. This was, after all, north Kensington which had a good track record of support for all kinds of social experiment. The most tolerant community in the world, or so I thought. I had misjudged our middle-class neighbours, alarmed at what might happen to the value of their houses if Lighthouse got going.

The Planning Officer posted public notices and wrote to people whose properties were nearby, telling them that if they had any objection to the proposed centre they should contact him at the Town Hall. To my astonishment there was an immediate explosion of anger in the community and in no time a vicious, well-orchestrated 'Stop London Lighthouse' bandwagon was rolling.

One morning I found a skull and crossbones on our front door with the slogan AIDS DEATH HOUSE scrawled underneath. We received homophobic telephone calls: 'It's not that I object to what you h-o-m-o-sexuals get up to in private, I just don't want my children caught in the crossfire when you get beaten up in the street.' For the first time as a gay man in London, I encountered hostility from people in the street, even from a neighbour with whom I had been on passing-the-time-of-the-day-over-the-garden-fence terms for years.

The Town Hall politicians were rattled by this turn of events and, ever cautious, they deferred a decision for two months. In the meantime, they suggested, perhaps London Lighthouse might get its community relations onto a better footing. A friend said, 'What you must do in a situation like this, Christopher, is to convene a public meeting. I'll give you two bits of advice, hold it in a church and ask a clergyman to take the chair. People will behave better.' I followed this advice and asked my good friend Richard Adfield, a local Anglican vicar, if he would chair the meeting, now fixed to take place in the Ecumenical Church in Lancaster Road in a week's time. Supportive as always, Richard agreed.

Meanwhile the media descended on Notting Hill. Suddenly every newspaper was carrying this NIMBY story about a row over the siting of an AIDS hospice. TV film crews walked up and down Lancaster Road interviewing local residents. Journalists started to telephone asking for interviews. Would we take part in a TV studio discussion show, could BBC Radio come and do a piece?

We did our best, but we just weren't prepared for this and it was all a bit disconcerting. Then a friend cheered me up by pointing out that this was terrific exposure for Lighthouse, 'If you spent a million pounds on PR, you couldn't hope for coverage like this.' How right he was. Both these apparent reverses, the local opposition and the media onslaught, were very short-lived and had marvellous consequences. The opposition melted away as quickly as it had been whipped up and the media attention put London Lighthouse on the map, starting a groundswell of support from far and wide.

The public meeting was packed to the gallery. I guessed 50-50: roughly half pro-Lighthouse, the ranks swelled by the gay community, loyally turning out from all over town; and half anti, mostly locals, grim-faced and tense. To prevent a circus and to promote dialogue, I decided to exclude television cameras.

I was to speak first. Terrified, I stumbled through somehow. At least I stuck fast to our policy of never attacking back no matter what hostility we might encounter. My gist was that given the nature of AIDS, people's fears about the Lighthouse proposal were perfectly understandable though unfounded. In fact there was nothing to fear, whether we liked it or not the epidemic was right here in this community and had been for several years. Now we had to come to terms with it, making decent provision for people's needs. If things weren't right for people living with AIDS in our community then things weren't, in fact, right for anyone else either.

At least I was given a more or less attentive hearing. Not so poor Dr Tony Pinching, then a consultant immunologist at St Mary's Hospital, who had agreed to come and reassure people, lending the voice of medical authority to the facts about AIDS. No sooner had he got to his

feet than a man in the gallery stood up and started yelling. 'Don't you
dare stand there telling us there is no danger from AIDS', he screamed,
repeating himself over and over again until Tony had to give up and sit
down, defeated.

When the meeting was thrown open to the floor many people
spoke, both for and against Lighthouse. First a local social worker spoke
in impassioned support. She was followed by a local councillor, also
more or less in support (though she did emphasise that these poor AIDS
victims would after all be securely behind walls out of harm's way, so
really there was no need for alarm). Next a couple of the opposition
ringleaders took the line that of course people with AIDS needed care,
but this area with all its problems - drug addicts, dirty needles in the
street, gay men and sundry other undifferentiated horrors - was hardly
the place. Wouldn't somewhere out in the countryside be altogether
more suitable? And so it went on, every speaker having to endure their
share of barracking from the other side.

An elderly woman stood up and walked to the front of the church.
She spoke slowly, quietly and with great dignity. 'I arrived in this country
as a refugee in the Second World War', she said, 'escaping with my sister
on the last children's train out of Czechoslovakia where the rest of my
family perished. I find it very hard to understand how it is that you, the
people of this country who reached out the hand of welcome to me, a
foreigner, then, won't now look after your own.' In silence, she started to
walk back to her seat.

But in a moment the silence was broken. A man stood up, gave the
Nazi salute and shouted, 'Heil Hitler!'

Then Ann Holmes, later a local Labour party parliamentary
candidate, lightened things with a robust defence of gay men, loudly
cheered from the gallery. If gay men were such a menace in this
community, she wondered, how was it that her teenage son could walk
the streets without, to her certain knowledge, even once being harassed
by a gay man, while she and her daughter were constantly having to
contend with the unwanted attentions of heterosexual men?

We were over the worst. A 'Support London Lighthouse' campaign
got underway that night, quickly overtaking the opposition. As well as
hundreds of individuals, between 70 and 80 local organisations wrote to
the Planning Officer in support. Signatures were collected for a petition
which was presented at the Town Hall by a deputation of local residents,
including the father of a young man who had recently died of AIDS.

The politicians were reassured and the planning application was
approved. Before long the Royal Borough made a lead donation to the

capital appeal of £100,000, an unheard-of sum in those days, and it has championed the Lighthouse ever since. The man who screamed at Tony Pinching became a stalwart supporter and still lives nearby. The leader of the opposition sold her house across the street to the publisher Carmen Calill and moved away. Carmen got a bargain and Lighthouse a much more agreeable neighbour. The media remained interested and, as our bulging file of press cuttings shows, mainly on our side.

People thinking of setting up an HIV/AIDS project in their area often ask me how to avoid the kind of opposition we had to face. I say, 'You can't, you just have to meet it.' The attitudes which fuel such a reaction are there, lurking under the surface in every community. But if people are given the chance to air their prejudice and express their fear, and are listened to with respect rather than attacked, then they can move on to adopt another point of view. If our experience at Lighthouse is any guide, such people, liberated a little by a fresh and more human perspective, may even become the staunchest supporters.

Chapter 6
Only the Best

irst-time visitors to the Lighthouse often walk right past the centre, not because it is easy to miss but because they cannot imagine that an AIDS project could be housed in such a magnificent building. Surely, they say to themselves, London Lighthouse must be on down the street in some suitably anonymous, seedy, down-at-heel building.

Two much-recited injunctions from childhood stick in my mind. 'If a job's worth doing, it's worth doing well', and, probably because I come from a naval tradition on both sides of my family, 'never lose the ship for a ha'porth o'tar.' But we were after something more than just a quality job for the Lighthouse. We wanted to make a resounding statement that this issue of AIDS and everyone touched by it matters, that only the best is good enough.

In its present state of decay, the building certainly had a long way to go, so our next task was drawing up a tender brief and appointing architects. We wanted the design to express the philosophy of the project and our approach to care. It must confirm the value of everyone. It must be domestic rather than institutional. It must not sweep death, or the process of dying, out of sight. In order to challenge the medicalisation of AIDS, it must be personal rather than clinical. It must empower people to make their own choices and to take responsibility for their own decisions. It had to be proud, accessible and safe. It was a tall order.

Several firms expressed interest and an afternoon was set aside for their presentations. The first five were predictable but unexciting. Some made it very clear that we had no idea what we were taking on (which was possibly true but tactless to point out), some brought models to show how fire doors would be sited, beds arranged, wheelchairs stored. None lit a spark.

Then came the sixth group, from a firm called First Architecture, armed with no written proposal, drawings or models. 'We have absolutely no idea what we would do with your building,' they said, 'we have never done anything like it before, but we are very interested in the idea of the Lighthouse and want to tell you how we would approach the task.' They told us they would begin with a consultation exercise involving as wide a range of interested parties as possible so that the design of the building reflected the views of those who would actually use it. This sounded an exciting approach and consistent with our philosophy of people living with the virus being at the centre of things. So First Architecture won the contract and, to our good fortune, the project leader was Robert Sproson.

Another meeting was convened. This time it took place in the former synagogue at the back of the derelict school. Out of the blue a generous stranger rang up offering to prepare and donate a boxed picnic lunch for the occasion. About 50 people assembled, the architectural team, ourselves, people in the network living with HIV/AIDS, partners and family members, doctors, nurses, clergy and an assortment of other supporters. I introduced the architects and outlined the principles on which we were trying to develop the project, the consultation exercise was introduced and a questionnaire explained. People were to be divided up into small groups and dates set for meetings with Robert Sproson. For what seemed to me like weeks, invariably in smoke-filled rooms, we met to brainstorm every conceivable aspect of the building design.

When at last it was over, Robert Sproson and his team analysed the mass of data collected and produced the first drawings. Looking back it is encouraging to see just how well the basic design of the building has worked for its purpose. This is still true ten years on even though growth in the organisation and changing needs have meant constant remodelling. I believe this has everything to do with listening so thoroughly at the very beginning to the people the building was intended for, to what they thought, hoped for and needed.

Robert's design was astonishing. On paper at least the old school was transformed and scarcely recognisable. Critics had said it was quite unsuitable, far too big for our purpose and why couldn't we start more modestly, for example in a house? Now here it was larger still, almost double the size of the original building, 31,000 square feet. What would people say now, and where would we find the money?

In Robert's design, where the school playground had been, behind that hideous perimeter wall, there is now a beautiful, rounded three-storey front, a graphic interpretation of the arc of light that radiates from a lighthouse. It brings the building - and with it of course the issue - out to the street, right where it belongs. On either side of the glass front door are curved walls representing arms outstretched in welcome. At the sides are huge windows reaching to the very top of the building, through which light pours in. That perimeter wall has been replaced by elegant railings, reassuring the passer-by that there is nothing to hide.

Attaching the new front to the original building is a glass atrium, with glazed bridges linking the two parts on the first and second floors. Wherever you may be in this building you feel connected with all its parts and you can see the sky. Neither people nor functions are isolated from each other. Gone is the flaking white paint, revealing soft pink brick and for the first time handsome detail in the windows and doorways of the original building. Gone is an ugly first floor flat at the back above the synagogue, replaced by a handsome three-storey wing, with south-facing conservatories on the ground and top floors.

The old synagogue has been transformed into a well-proportioned meeting hall, reduced in size to create space on the ground floor for a quiet room and on the first floor for a mortuary and viewing room. A single-storey kitchen wing has been added at ground level looking onto the garden and, complementing the bow front, a perpendicular tower houses the lift-shaft. Inside, natural materials, shape, colour, space and scale work in harmony to communicate welcome, accessibility, safety, connection, intimacy to everyone who enters. As Tony Chard, a member of staff who died in 1995, eloquently expressed it, 'From the minute you walk in you are faced with the sometimes disturbing fact that you matter profoundly.'

Light, curves, circles, glass, ash, terracotta and blue, it is a confection of beauty, in every way a building to encourage hope and lift the human spirit. Just what was wanted, more than we hoped for; at last, a lighthouse.

Chapter 7
Act of Faith

'It's very refreshing to find the word ... er ... er ... *love*, in a grant application', commented one of the officials seated round a table in Alexander Fleming House at the Elephant and Castle, architecturally one of London's worst nightmares.

I had not been in the building since the sixties when Task Force, the organisation I then worked for, published a report about the growing scandal of hypothermia among the elderly, *Old and Cold in Islington*. This caused something of a stir and we were summoned to a ministerial meeting with the then Secretary of State, Sir Keith Joseph. The old place hadn't aged too well.

Andrew Henderson, Mary Pipes, our newly-appointed fundraiser, and I were at the Department of Health to make a presentation in support of our bid for funding under the government's Section 64 allocation to the voluntary sector. On our way there Mary found an error in our submission, so we had to stop at a shop and buy Tipp-ex, correcting all the copies over an anxious cappuccino.

I was a bit taken aback by the sheer number of civil servants. Over the years since I have got used to this in my dealings with the statutory sector. It takes a lot of well-paid people to tell you that your proposal is unaffordable. But they were friendly enough and gave us a reasonable hearing, apparently receptive to our plans for the Lighthouse.

Suddenly there's a question hanging in the air, 'How much?' Andrew looks at me, I look at Mary and Mary looks back at me. 'Well,' I venture, 'we're working on a ball-park figure of £2 million and, if the government will commit £1 million, we will raise the rest.' 'A million pounds!' exclaims Mr Money-bags, peering at me across the table over a pair of half-moon spectacles identical to my father's. 'Really, Mr Spence, we had in mind a figure much more in the order of £10,000.'

This was late autumn and we were in a hurry to start building work. But the government just wasn't going to be rushed and, month after month, we heard nothing definite. Luckily we had found contractors willing to come on site without guarantees of when we would be in a position to pay them, so work began anyway. One day the streets around the Lighthouse had to be closed for the arrival on site of an 80-foot-high crane. To me this was not only the biggest, but also quite the most beautiful crane in the whole world. On 5 August 1987, Lighthouse's first birthday, I climbed to the top and felt like a trapeze artist without a safety net. From my house across the street, the sound of pneumatic drills was music to my ears. Well, to begin with anyway.

What our contractors, Wiltshier's, hadn't told us - or perhaps I just failed to take it in - was that if building works had to be called to a halt at any stage, in the unhappy event, say, of non-payment of bills, then this would cost in the region of £200,000. There are some things it is better not to know until after the event.

I figured we had nothing to lose and that the more advanced the project, the less the chance of it collapsing for lack of funds. This proved to be true as far as most funding sources were concerned; one grant led to another, each successful fundraising event inspired the next, every donor recruited others. So the capital appeal was gathering momentum.

But there was no shortage of sceptics telling us that there just wasn't the kind of money we were after and that the appeal was quite likely to run out of steam before we had raised even a million pounds. I wasn't prepared to contemplate that, but I did know that we must secure the support of central government if there was any hope of reaching our target. Besides, it seemed to me right and proper that Lighthouse should be funded substantially from the public purse.

Then we had a stroke of luck. In May 1987 Margaret Thatcher called a general election. Here was my chance. I rang the Department of Health and explained that we were not in a position to pay the builders and that unless there was an immediate injection of capital I would have no alternative but to call the building programme to a halt. For a government proud of its record on the issue of HIV/AIDS, that wouldn't look too good in the middle of a general election campaign, now would it? Next day the government announced a capital grant to London Lighthouse of £500,000. A crisis was averted and for the moment at least we were out of the wood. But not for very long.

Costs soon began to escalate. With capital schemes, I now apply the principle that projected costs will end up being roughly double the figure you first thought of, but I hadn't learnt that yet. Our ball-park figure of £2 million finally rose to £4.85 million. Perhaps it was better not to have known that at the start either.

Enter Ian McKellen. He rang up one day and told me that he had just come back from touring his one-man show *Acting Shakespeare* in the United States of America and that he wasn't working for the moment. Could he put on the show in a West End theatre and donate all the money to Lighthouse? Given another looming cash crisis, a seemingly unbridgeable gap between the bill we were expecting from the builders shortly and the money we had in the bank, this sounded too good to be true.

The show played to packed houses and included a gala performance attended by Princess Margaret. 'Now don't forget to ask me to open the Lighthouse when the time comes', she said as she took her leave. True to her word, she performed the opening ceremony and she has been our loyal supporter ever since, turning out whenever we've asked, twice even coming to the circus at midnight in the depths of winter. And on World AIDS Day in 1992, she announced that she had agreed to be our Royal Patron.

At the end of every performance Ian McKellen came on stage, spoke movingly about the issue of AIDS and about Lighthouse, and then stood about in the foyer, dressed in a Lighthouse T-shirt with dozens of other volunteers, rattling buckets and hustling donations. By end of a seven-week run, nearly £500,000 had been raised. Now we could pay the builders and I could go back to the Department of Health and say, 'Look at the commitment to complete this project out there, now the government *must* do more.' And more they did. Timed to coincide with a meeting of European health ministers on AIDS, fortuitously taking place in London early in the new year, the government announced a further capital grant to London Lighthouse of £750,000. We were nearly there.

It had been an exhilarating and exhausting 18 months. Apart from the health service, local authorities and the government, who between them produced about £2.5 million, and generous support from a number of charitable trusts, notably Simon Sainsbury's Monument Trust, it had been a marathon effort on the part of literally thousands of people.

The Princess of Wales and the Duchess of York turned out for auctions of contemporary works of art and other treasures, including a David Hockney painting and Elizabeth Taylor's jewellery, all of which raised hundreds of thousands of pounds. The Princess of Wales was to be a fast friend to Lighthouse, as well as to the wider world of HIV and AIDS, becoming Patron of the National AIDS Trust and undertaking numerous public engagements on behalf of Lighthouse and other projects. She has visited Lighthouse unofficially on many occasions since, skilfully making a most personal connection with all those she meets and never failing to raise everyone's spirits.

Kurt Weill's splendid opera *Street Scene* was performed for the first time in this country as a benefit for Lighthouse. London galleries got together to donate enough artworks to decorate the building. Manufacturers gave us furniture, fittings and generous discounts. An anonymous donor gave us a priceless Bechstein grand piano which stands today in the acoustically perfect former synagogue, now renamed the Ian McKellen Hall.

There were small fundraising events almost every day somewhere in London or elsewhere across the country. Schools, churches, pubs, clubs, theatre groups, cabaret artists, cartoonists, musicians, conjurors, shops, restaurants, cinemas, office parties, barn dances, drag balls, raffles and sponsored feats of all kinds, including a parachute jump - everyone did their bit.

I got some stick from sections of the gay community for drawing the line at a boot-licking contest and a slave auction. Call me old-fashioned but I just couldn't quite square such events with what Lighthouse was trying to say, however heartfelt the offer.

Best of all were the individual donations and the letters which people sent with them. Reading those letters helped me through many tough moments. And there was a legacy from Graham Gardner, who hadn't lived to see the building finished. But he came to live with me in the last few months of his life and proudly claimed the status of 'first Lighthouse resident' anyway.

In June 1988, just 22 months from the day we purchased the derelict school, we began to occupy parts of the building. Miraculously, Lighthouse was never once overdrawn at the bank and we opened our doors with no debt.

I think that word *love* was about right, don't you?

Chapter 8
Danger

Towards the end of 1987 I sniffed danger in the wind. It had been quite a year. After more than 20 years together, Andrew Henderson and I parted. He moved out of our house in Lancaster Road to live temporarily with friends nearby. My initiative, the split had been a long time coming but it was painful just the same. We worked hard to keep the changes in our relationship and our collaboration over Lighthouse separate and the effort paid off. Lighthouse could not have had a finer founding Chair for its Council of Management, nor I as Director a wiser, kinder and more loyal boss.

On top of the demands of the capital appeal, I was managing a growing group of staff working on three sites. Work to commission the building and design the services was gathering momentum and by now the home support service was up and running. I also had a full schedule of classes, support groups and workshops, including trips to lead 'Life, Death and the Challenge of AIDS' in Sweden, Switzerland and the United States of America.

Graham Gardner moved into the Lancaster Road house to live with me, now extremely frail and in need of a good deal of care and emotional support. Apart from my bedroom and bathroom, Lighthouse gradually took over the rest of the house. At times it seemed rather like living in a mainline railway station. Apart from work my life was on hold.

One night I came up from the basement where I had been teaching a class. There was an urgent message on the answerphone, would I go at once to be with Michael, a member of the network who was dying? I checked that Graham was comfortable, left him my telephone number just in case and set off. I stayed all night and Michael died at eight o'clock the next morning. I then rushed back home to bath, change and get ready to join Mary Pipes for a meeting with funders.

'You may find some of our questions rather trying,' warned the Grants Officer, 'the fact is that we prefer to satisfy ourselves before approving grants, rather than having to pick up the pieces later, when projects have fallen to bits because they're not being properly run, particularly projects with *charismatic* leadership.' Oh dear, I thought, glancing at Mary Pipes in alarm, so charismatic is not the thing to be. 'Yes, I understand,' I replied, 'and I can assure you that we don't go in for charismatic leadership at London Lighthouse.'

Instead of any discussion about HIV/AIDS and our work, there followed an interrogation of unbelievable detail. Who handles the petty cash and how is it recorded? Who buys the postage stamps? Does the project pay rent for its accommodation? To whom are the cheques made out and who signs them? On and on and on it goes.

My mind drifted back to the scene in Michael's bedroom. Suddenly I felt the room starting to revolve slowly. Was this terminal boredom or was my sleepless night beginning to catch up with me? 'I wonder if we could possibly have a cup of coffee?', I asked. Someone was despatched to bring coffee and, while we were waiting, I smiled at the Grants Officer, thinking I should offer an explanation for disrupting the meeting. 'I'm awfully sorry but I'm feeling a bit fragile. I was up all night with a friend who died at eight o'clock this morning.' 'Yes indeed,' came the impassive reply, 'now, if we can turn to the figures on page eight of your grant application?'

There's death literacy for you. Never mind, we got our grant.

Nancy and I led a new year workshop, 'Visions, Dreams and Goals'. I wasn't very interested in people's goals. Mine didn't extend further than the holiday we were taking afterwards in Madeira. I was exhausted. Tired leadership can't, of course, remain much good for long. I knew this was dangerous for the health of the project, but the danger I sensed now was more than just fatigue.

For about ten years before starting Lighthouse I had been active in an international counselling organisation known as Re-evaluation Counselling. Its method, co-counselling, had been invaluable in helping me break through pathological anxiety and fear, develop a stronger sense of myself, trust my own thinking, and focus my commitment to social change. I had also become a skilled counsellor.

Although I took issue with aspects of the theory, it gave me a grounding in the mechanisms of oppression, structural and personal, which still informs my work. In due course leading in the organisation helped me develop as a communicator, trainer and group facilitator. On all of this I have drawn gratefully ever since, not least in developing the support network from which Lighthouse came.

Which is where the danger now lay. Full of good people as it was, seekers after truth and social activists, organisationally Re-evaluation Counselling was cultish, corrupt and contradictory, facts it took me many years to uncover and understand. Dominated by an autocratic, grandiose, controlling leader, like every cult, its followers were enslaved in the name of freedom. Apparently promoting the capacity of members to think for themselves on every issue, in fact it told them what to think.

Affection alternating with abuse, vendettas against dissenters, strict censorship, sexual exploitation of women and homophobic policies were some of the results. As I discovered through introducing friends living with the virus, the organisation was also subtly death-denying and at one point the leader even advocated enforced quarantine for people living with HIV and AIDS.

In setting out to build an organisation to meet the challenge of AIDS, one which I knew must grow big and strong very fast, how was I to protect it from the danger of becoming a cult? How was this to be avoided, especially when I, its director, was also the now somewhat *guru-ised* leader of the support network out of which it had grown? How was I going to build a healthy organisation, incorporating only good principles and practice learnt from Re-evaluation Counselling, and discarding the rest?

People were already talking about 'belonging' to the Lighthouse 'community', with its connotations of membership. The word 'family' was also becoming common currency. If Lighthouse became something, a cult, a church, a community, call it what you will, which you had to 'join', then by definition many from the wide diversity of people entitled to use it would feel and find themselves excluded. This was worrying.

I went off to Madeira with Nancy, tired, tense and numb. As always she was wonderful; loving, patient, attentive. After a few days a dam burst and I started to cry.

Nancy: 'What are the words?'

Me: 'I don't want to live like this any more.'

Nancy: 'How do you want to live?'

Me: 'I don't know … but I want to see the spring.'

Nancy: 'When you think about seeing the spring, what do you see?'

Me: 'The garden in Oxfordshire.'

Slowly, slowly, I began to think previously unthinkable thoughts. Could I live in the country and travel in to London every day? Could I do this work, build this new organisation *and* have an ordinary home life? Could I do one job and do it well, rather than be wiped out struggling to do several not very well? Could I, for the first time in my life, live alone for a while? Could I even start gardening again? This was a revelation. But so it came about.

I completed my schedule of teaching commitments, making it clear that I would not be taking on any more. I started refusing invitations to lead international workshops. I resigned from one or two organisations in the community. A lot of people in the network felt bitterly disappointed and betrayed. I was attacked for taking Lighthouse away from its core values and for abandoning the network which had inspired it. I took this as confirmation of my suspicion that, unwittingly and with the best of intentions, in the name of empowerment I had in fact fostered some unhealthy dependence on myself as leader of the network. If this was so, people were bound to suffer painful withdrawal symptoms. And they did.

Good things came of it too. John Shine, a member of the founding group and our first paid employee, whose heart was I think always in therapy rather than in building an organisation on the scale of Lighthouse, left to found the Red Admiral Project which to this day provides a first-class HIV/AIDS counselling service. Although at the time this was a sad parting of the ways, John and I have remained good friends and we see each other regularly, enjoying animated conversations about our respective work. In the course of time most of those who drifted away in disappointment found their way back into relationship with Lighthouse and with me, and I think on a much better footing.

In April I packed and moved out of the house in Lancaster Road, letting it to a group of nurses working at the Lighthouse until in due course Andrew reoccupied it himself. I took up permanent residence in Oxfordshire, taking to commuting happily and enjoying more time with my parents who were by now beginning to fail.

For the first time in many years, I had a full-time job. I was excited, instead of overwhelmed, at the prospect of building a new, robustly healthy organisation, one which would not be pathologically dependent on me, one in which people could think for themselves.

I loved living alone. I began to feel like an ordinary human being again. I did my shopping in the village. I made new friends. In the evenings and at weekends I started to garden. Lighthouse had a director, not a guru. I had a life. It was magic.

Chapter 9
On the Edge of the Ocean

One Sunday in April 1988, which happened to be my 44th birthday, I drove up from the country to attend a party given by Carmen Calill. Having just moved in across the street, she was generously making her house-warming celebration a fundraising benefit for Lighthouse. London's *literati* were there in force and champagne was flowing.

When the merriment was well and truly underway, Carmen asked me to say a few words about the Lighthouse and then to take people on a conducted tour of the still unfinished building. Perhaps it was the champagne but suddenly, as if for the first time, I saw the impact all this was having on those present. Simon Callow recalled the occasion several years later in a radio broadcast saying, 'I was astonished, as anyone would be, by the extraordinary austere beauty and aesthetic simplicity of the building, and by this concept of a hospice which is beyond the idea of a hospice.'

Sometimes it is possible to see through the eyes of others what is too close to see through your own. I felt touched and proud, yet unexpectedly uneasy, apprehensive. Then a question flashed into my mind. If this building makes such a compelling statement, already, even before it is completed and occupied, what kind of organisation must we build if its work is to be a true expression of that statement? Our efforts to meet that challenge are the subject of the next part of this book, but already I knew that the task would not be easy.

About this time another generous benefactor to Lighthouse, the artist Howard Hodgkin, was painting an extraordinary picture. It is one of a number of paintings that he gave us permission to reproduce as greetings cards and sell to raise money for the project. It is called *On the Edge of the Ocean*, an almost overwhelming splash of power and colour and movement, vibrant blue waves and a shaft of brilliant red light streaming down from the sky.

I find the picture compelling, adventurous and hopeful. It calls to mind some lines from 'Little Gidding', one of T S Eliot's famous *Four Quartets*:

We shall not cease from exploration
And the end of all our exploring
Will be to arrive where we started
And know the place for the first time.

In parallel with commissioning the building, an immense task in itself, we were recruiting staff. At the end of 1987 the paid staff group had been small enough to sit down to Christmas lunch together round my dining table. By the end of 1988 there were more than a hundred people in paid posts, rising eventually to about 180. With the best will in the world it was impossible to get to know everyone well or to provide induction and training of the standard we expect today. We did the best we could but people had to fend for themselves, sink or swim.

We attempted a three-day large group induction workshop, adapted from 'Life, Death and the Challenge of AIDS'. For some it was a transformative experience, for others a nightmare. Philip Sanderson, the senior charge nurse who died in 1995, memorably 'came out' as HIV-positive for the first time in public. Later he wrote in *Lighthouse News* about how this had changed both his way of thinking and his life. But some people found the intensity too much to take: hadn't they, after all, contracted for a job of work, not a human growth programme? After this I left staff training to the training department.

Some appointments were very successful, others less so. With only intuition to inform the parameters of posts and with the organisation developing faster than we could keep pace with, we sometimes put square pegs in round holes. Or we found the hole we had thought required a round peg had, by the time the peg arrived, in fact become a square one. Or the size of the hole had grown so much in a few weeks that the wretched peg couldn't possibly fill it, only flop about instead. Earlier we had made one senior appointment, a general manager post, designed to take some of the load of operational management off my shoulders, but when this didn't work out well we created a single management tier instead. This was good for collective thinking, decision-making and mutual support, at least for a time, but it was cumbersome and it left me directly line-managing far too many people.

Meanwhile we began to occupy the building in stages. Particularly for those who had spent the previous 18 months working in three

Portakabins, stacked one on top of another, in the middle of the noisy, muddy building site, this was something of a culture shock. Throughout, the building was fitted out, decorated and furnished in superb style, thanks to the generosity of many of our suppliers. I decided that my office must be located somewhere in the very heart of the place. I thought the longer the walk through the centre, the better connected I could stay with the workforce and the greater the impact on visitors. To see me, visitors must pass through two entire floors, witnessing the centre 'teeming with messy life' as someone once said. Invariably, by the time they reach my office, the end of the line, the place has already begun to have its effect. This works well, particularly as far as fundraising is concerned. It is also on my long walks through the building, to and from my office, that I do much of my work informally - they call it MBWA (management by walking around). Over the years, I have resisted attempts to get me to move elsewhere.

By now everyone was installed under one roof, a luxury which wouldn't last very long, though we didn't know that yet. In addition to home support, a training programme was developed and the counselling service expanded. Finally the Residential Unit was finished and a full complement of nursing staff recruited, inducted and trained in the Lighthouse approach to care. This was the responsibility of Hamish MacGregor, the first head of the Unit, who now works part time as a trainer. It was nearly time to welcome our first residents.

A rich friend, Christopher Cowlin, had said to me at the very beginning of the capital appeal, 'When it's almost finished, come and tell me what you still need.' It was beds. We wanted a particular Swedish bed, costing about £2,000, which could be raised, lowered, tilted and so on, by the occupant operating the controls. This would mean people could be more in charge of their comfort and less dependent on the nursing staff. As good as his word, Christopher generously gave us the 23 beds. Ironically, when he arrived at the Lighthouse later that year to die himself, he found the bed too short for his considerable length and asked for his own bed to be brought in for him.

Thirty-one thousand square feet is a lot of space to occupy and it seemed as though we would never complete the task of moving in. One day Linda Durman, a member of our Council of Management, arrived for a meeting. 'How are things, Christopher?', she said. I told her that I would be thankful when we were through with all this upheaval and could really get on with the work of delivering services. 'But *that's* when things really begin to get difficult', said Linda. How right she was.

The long-awaited arrival of our first residents was not very successful. They were a couple with their dog. One was dying, the other very frail. Not everything worked as it should have done. The nursing care was erratic, call bells went unanswered, a muddle was made over drugs, the food was unappetising. The list of complaints was a long one and not only the residents, but also the neighbourhood team volunteers who were supporting this couple at home, were bitterly disappointed. I was sent an angry letter demanding redress. The letter detailing the complaints was circulated here, there and everywhere including to someone working in another HIV/AIDS organisation. That person immediately sent it on to the AIDS Unit at the Department of Health where in fact, as always, officials were entirely supportive. Not for the first or last time, I was reminded of what my former boss Selwyn Lloyd used to say apropos his sacking as Chancellor of the Exchequer in Harold Macmillan's Night of the Long Knives, 'Forgiveness is the sweetest form of revenge.' Painful as this episode was, it was a chance for everyone to learn some important lessons.

As we headed towards the official opening, it was time to open the building to public scrutiny and eventually to the press. Mary Pipes and Caspar Thomson, our Press/PR officer, suggested a series of open days for different interest groups. The format was not unlike the open days we still hold every Friday, except that at this stage it featured a tour of the building, including a visit to the mortuary and viewing room.

One such day was for the local community. The last headmaster of the Solomon Wolfson Jewish School and a man who had been a pupil in the school when it first opened on this site in 1929 both turned up, delighted to meet one another. After the tour, eyes shining, they came and told me what a transformation it was and how they had been unable to locate even one recognisable room. It was touching to see the good memories they both seemed to have of our building's earlier incarnation. It confirmed what I had always sensed, that it had 'good stones' and had been a happy place.

Another was a very well-attended day for clinicians. After I had done my presentation and they had returned from the tour, it was time for questions. A man stood up and said, 'I'm Dr So-and-so. I'm a consultant in genito-urinary medicine in the Midlands. I don't wish to cast a sour note and of course I'm all for people dying with dignity, but really this place is right over the top. It's much too lavish, more like a five-star hotel than a health care facility.'

For a moment I was stunned, frantically trying not to feel defensive, to marshal my facts and figures accurately; only £95 per square foot, including furnishings, much cheaper than an equivalent-sized purpose-built NHS facility, furnishings and equipment of high quality because so much of it has been donated, the difference is in the way the building has been thought about rather than the cost, and so on. I need not have worried. Another man stood up and said, 'I'm Dr Such-and-such. I'm from the north of England, also a consultant in genito-urinary medicine. I feel I must be very honest and tell you that the emotion I have had to contend with in seeing round this remarkable building this afternoon is envy. I feel envious because I know that every patient I treat under the National Health Service deserves this standard of care and I know they don't get it. I congratulate you on an extraordinary achievement.'

Soon all 23 beds were open. Drop-in services began to be put in place, a support and information service, legal advice, social and therapeutic activities, a daily exercise class. Complementary therapies were added to the menu of available services. Seminars and conferences were held, complementing the training programme. The café was opened, the garden planted.

It was time for the official opening. Princess Margaret fulfilled her promise and a red carpet was laid from the front door to the road. A few minutes before her arrival someone noticed that a car was parked askew actually on the red carpet, the driver nowhere to be seen. It turned out to belong to Addy Berman, a rather wild and eccentric user of Lighthouse. In his anxiety to position himself where he couldn't fail to meet the Princess, he had got a bit hasty. In a few minutes he was found and the car moved elsewhere just in time.

John Reid generously sent a car to fetch my father to the ceremony. From the start he had been unswerving in his support and interest, once saying to me, 'I think this work is very, very important. I only wish I could come to London myself and lend a hand.' My mother was in hospital and couldn't come. I was moved by the sight of this now frail old man, still holding himself like a soldier, wearing his regimental tie and emerging all alone from what turned out to be a cavernous stretch-limo, now taking up more than its fair share of parking space.

Dignitaries, funders, friends and special guests took their places. Speeches were made and photographs taken. Princess Margaret toured the building and took tea in the café meeting residents, staff and guests. After listening attentively to well-rehearsed presentations about the community services and training departments, she summarised the work of each with memorable economy, 'Yes, I see, moral support and discussion.'

Oddly, or perhaps it's no chance, the outside front wall of the original building, now part of the reception area, had two stones, one detailing the Solomon Wolfson Jewish School's foundation, the other left blank, waiting. Now a glass panel had been placed over the second stone. In letters of Lighthouse blue, the inscription reads:

REBUILT BY MANY HANDS
FOR
LONDON LIGHTHOUSE
A CENTRE FOR PEOPLE FACING THE CHALLENGE OF AIDS

Three years, five months and 23 days after Frank's death, London Lighthouse was formally declared open. We had arrived safely where we started. Now it was time to embark on another long voyage.

Chapter 10
Safety's Shore

At lunchtime on the day of the Royal Opening of London Lighthouse, 23 November 1988, Nancy and I were snatching a few quiet moments in my office before changing our clothes and going on parade for the official ceremony. Quietly she said, 'May I please read you something? It's a poem I've been writing. It's to you.'

April 1985, you called.
You'd briefly left Frank's side, a vigil which
A fortnight you had kept: a well of light
For him, a true reflecting back his love,
A clear-cast beacon sent from safety's shore.
Your tenderness, your fearless, loving touch,
Your seeing the sweet soul of innocence
He was. You'd heard his tears, and through the drugs
And through the barriers of masks and gloves
You held him. And you said to me that you'd
Not rest until the hospital and staff,
And all its disconnected policies,
And each impediment to death's own pace,
The fear the very word AIDS resurrects,
Were wholly changed and gay men dignified,
And dying seen as part of living well,
And every myth of AIDS fully dispelled.
You raged and grieved and there a dream conceived.
You charted course. You set sail. You believed.
And now November 1988

The love you cast for Frank lights up the land.
And people hand in hand sail safely home,
And tier to tier the glass well fills with light,
Embraced and free they do not fear the night.
With death a time of dignity and peace
Step by step we see oppression cease.
And hospitals and doctors down the line
See love and death and health are woven fine
And terracotta, circles of ash and blue
Embrace, caress and sing love songs to you.

A calligrapher friend copied it exquisitely onto parchment: terracotta, cream and azure letters on a Lighthouse blue background. Mounted in ivory in a gilt frame, it hangs in our house in Oxfordshire. It never fails to move me to tears.

Part 2

Not just a model of care, more a way of thinking

Lift up your faces, you have a piercing need
For this bright morning dawning for you.
History, despite its wrenching pain,
Cannot be unlived, but if faced
With courage, need not be lived again.

Lift up your eyes
Upon this day breaking for you.
Give birth again
To the dream.

From
On the Pulse of Morning
by Maya Angelou

(Read by the poet at
the Inauguration of
William Jefferson Clinton
20 January 1993)

Chapter 11
Safer Than a Known Way

What shape shall Lighthouse be? Structurally and organisationally, how shall we express our vision and values? I spent the ten years prior to starting Lighthouse working as a consultant in all kinds of organisations in the public, private and voluntary sectors in Britain and abroad. A fascinating time in many ways and doubtless good training for what was to come, it didn't inspire me to want ever again to be employed in an organisation, much less start one.

On bad days I think organisations are one of life's most regrettable necessities. Impossibly complex, dynamics murky and swirling, resistant to change, they often bring out the worst in people, not the best. But to organise in the modern world, to bring about social change, as far as I can tell they're essential. Anyway here I am trying to build one, whether I like it or not, so I had better give it my best shot. There are many factors to take into account.

Our 'core business', the primary task we are here to do, is providing services for people affected by HIV and AIDS. If there is to be any point in Lighthouse being the provider, rather than the statutory sector, then those services must be tip-top, distinctive, well-organised, high-quality. In the interest of efficiency will that mean a bureaucracy? Not my favourite concept.

If predictions are anything to go by, numbers are rising fast so the organisation will need to grow quickly and its constituency, now almost entirely white gay men, and workforce diversify. If it's to provide high-quality services *and* manage rapid growth, structurally Lighthouse must be strong and stable, especially taking account of its youth and inexperience, and of the level of turbulence in the HIV/AIDS sector.

Better not a democratic membership organisation then, with policy vulnerable to the vicissitudes and whims of a volatile, fickle electorate. Instead a carefully constructed Council of Management, responsible for setting overall policy, delegating day-to-day management of Lighthouse to a director and management team. Looking round the sector there are already organisations in trouble, just not built for bad weather. Those who sit on the Council, technically elected by themselves, double as directors of the company, legally Lighthouse's only 'members', and trustees of the charity. Two challenges here, achieving diversity in what is after all a 'self-perpetuating oligarchy' and ensuring that accountability is exercised down, as well as up and across the organisation. Later we successfully enlarged the Council through advertisement and a process in line with staff recruitment, in this way increasing diversity and adding to the number of HIV-positive members.

Funding: it is clear that Lighthouse is affordable only if its revenue is largely derived from the public purse. If it is to be 'bolted in' to the broad spectrum of statutory health and social care and win the confidence of budget-holders, then it must be structurally and organisationally *coherent* to public funding sources, all traditional, bureaucratic hierarchies.

A hierarchy then? Experience has taught me that hierarchies generally work best as far as the *task* is concerned. Well-defined structures, clarity about roles, responsibilities, authority in decision-making, lines of accountability, all this provides a framework for efficiency and cost-effectiveness, for successful outcomes. But what about quality of life in the workplace? Here hierarchies don't score so well. Is a hierarchy the best model for an HIV/AIDS organisation, especially one with its focus on empowerment? Isn't empowering people precisely what hierarchies don't generally do? How can a hierarchical structure encourage people to do their own thinking, to make mistakes, to develop autonomy? After all, isn't this what lies at the heart of empowerment?

Since HIV is a virus which attacks the immune system and undermines the capacity of the body to fend off infection, organisationally Lighthouse must be immuno-supportive, not immuno-suppressive. Is setting up a hierarchy the best way and what would an immuno-supportive organisation look and feel like anyway?

Recently I gave a lift in my car to a senior civil servant, with whom I was attending a meeting. Knowing his department, like much of the civil service, is undergoing a programme of down-sizing, reorganisation and redundancies, and that this is proving stressful for staff at every level, I asked him how things were going. 'Fine', he said. 'Well, fine as far as I know.' 'How's morale in the department, James?', I asked. 'How are people coping with the reductions in staffing and so much structural change?' 'To tell you the truth, I don't really know', he replied. 'I prefer not to ask. You see, if one asks then people will actually tell one and then one just might have to do something about it. I think it's much better not to know.' Immuno-supportive? Empowering? An attentive, safe and welcoming environment? It is easy to see what such an organisation wouldn't look like, but perhaps the civil service isn't after all the place to look for inspiration.

Then there's our commitment to challenge oppression, discrimination and prejudice, to speak up for social justice. If we structure Lighthouse like a mainstream bureaucracy, one that can fend for itself in the oppressive society, won't it risk simply becoming just another microcosm of that society? Won't it in the end internalise the prejudice, denial and fear it exists to challenge, becoming rigid and self-serving in the process?

What about keeping people living with HIV and AIDS central in the organisation, influencing policy and service development, actively contributing to the decision-making process? Won't setting up Lighthouse as a bureaucratic hierarchy be the best possible way of *not* achieving this? How will those at the top of the hierarchy, with their focus on funding and on planning for the future, avoid becoming remote and disconnected from the views of the people who probably know best what the organisation should be and do, those living with the virus?

Growth won't be the only change factor, there will also be constant loss and death. How will we handle that? Won't emotional support for the workforce need to be woven right into the fabric? If denial of death - that cosy sitting on the teapot of oppression keeping it brewing so nicely - is to be challenged, and the issue brought out into the open where it belongs, what will that mean organisationally? How can 'death literacy' be learnt and put into practice? I don't know any models.

In the wake of the collapse of Frontliners, the first UK coalition of people living with HIV and AIDS, the Department of Health commissioned the Compass Partnership to undertake an investigation into the causes and write a report. The report was brief, to the point and full of common sense. Take careful account, it said, of your project's stage of development. Is it an infant, toddler, teenager or young adult? Or is it in the middle years, even grand old age? Remember its needs will differ at every stage. Identify your project's purpose. What is its task? Whatever it is, do *that* and don't be diverted. And then structure accordingly.

Of course. That's it. Why not start thinking about the organisation as you would about a person? At what stage of development is this particular individual, in this case Lighthouse? What then are its real needs? How best can those needs be met? Isn't this the way to make sure, whatever the scale and pace of change, we never forget that Lighthouse, and AIDS itself, in the first place concerns people? Behind the quaint language of organisations - financial accountability, strategic planning, occupancy levels, data-gathering, monitoring and evaluation - it is people, of all sorts and in large numbers, who are at the heart of what is given and received at Lighthouse. Why not begin thinking about the organisation itself as a person, a person who matters, a person deserving time and attention, a person with a job to do and with needs to be met?

I realised I had been thinking in terms of alternatives; hierarchy or collective; autocracy or democracy; bureaucracy or chaotic free-for-all. But isn't empowerment refusing to accept we can't have everything? If hierarchy is necessary so that Lighthouse can accomplish its task effectively, can survive and thrive in the real world, perhaps it is nothing to fear? Why not start considering it *neutral*, with the potential to be whatever we want it to be, and then start thinking afresh? Thinking fresh seems to me a much, much safer way to proceed; besides isn't thinking for ourselves the point? This second part of the book describes some of the steps we've taken along the road.

Now on good days, more than seven years later, I still find thinking with others about how to make Lighthouse work, in accomplishing what it is here to do and in human terms too, the most tantalising, absorbing and rewarding challenge I can possibly imagine.

Chapter 12
Blocks and Tackle

I t was the actress Juliet Stevenson, visiting Lighthouse one World AIDS Day, who said, 'This isn't just a model of care, it's more a way of thinking.' Action, we say, can only be as good as the thinking behind it. Thinking can only be as good as the way we treat one another. Good, clear, *fresh* thinking, in such dangerously short supply the world over, emerges not by chance but under very specific circumstances.

Since it's good thinking we need if we're to have any hope of doing our job, of going the length in meeting this challenge of AIDS, our task is to create such circumstances at Lighthouse. This means doing whatever is possible to take away the blocks to people thinking well, above all thinking for themselves. I believe physical environment plays a big part in how well people can think and, without question, our building does some of the work for us, reflecting the philosophy as it does so beautifully. It sings that people matter, it bathes everyone in light, it beckons us to do whatever we're doing as well as we possibly can. It entices thinking.

Once installed, we set up that 'traditional' line management structure, only with some less traditional elements. The Council delegates day-to-day running of the project to senior management, a team of four led by the director. I line-manage an executive director, Susie Parsons, who line-manages two assistant directors, Judy Wolfram and Gráinne Morby. They line-manage 14 departmental heads who in turn line-manage the project's 500 paid and unpaid staff, often through 'fourth tier' managers. People need parameters in order to think well and this structure sets a clear framework, boundaries, for who is responsible for what and to whom, and for cascading information through the organisation efficiently.

But in tension with this pyramidal structure, guarding against the danger of rigidity and non-thinking, we hold three vital principles.

These are the right of everyone to maximum autonomy in the way they do their work, including the right to make mistakes. No mistakes, no experiment, no new learning about how to make things work well. Before very long, no new ideas either. People sometimes imagine that autonomy and accountability can't go hand in hand. 'If I'm allowed to do it my way, how can I be held accountable?' I answer, 'Given your particular job, let's agree *what* you are going to do and by when, then you think out *how* best to do it (and I'll help you think about that if you want me to). Then, together, we can measure the outcome against your targets.'

Then the right of everyone to say what they think on every issue. It's true that there have been times when, in the heat of battle, I've secretly wished this was not a guiding principle. But how can we hope to make decisions that are in the best interests of everyone, unless we ask them, and then pay attention to what they think? Policy development goes through consultative stages, working its way through the 'cycle' of relevant meetings. First draft, discussion, suggested amendments; if necessary, a second draft, discussion, more amendments; final draft, discussion, final amendments, decision, implementation. It is sometimes slow but in the end it works because the policy has wide ownership. Even though everyone may not agree with everything in it, at least everyone knows what the policy says and has had the chance to express a view.

The third principle is the right of everyone to good training, personal development and emotional support. People think best when they feel valued, when their needs are paid careful attention. These needs include acquiring tools for the job; expanding horizons, learning new insights, perspectives, expertise; opportunities to keep developing. To keep thinking people also need access to support in dealing with the emotional implications of work which takes us to the edge of life itself. The work concerns people and it won't be good work unless we make real relationships. If the relationship is real, then when one person dies, the other is bereaved.

Putting these principles into practice means a more participative framework than the structure might, at first glance, suggest. Much of the work is done in meetings, the focus of chapter 13, in team meetings, working parties, action teams and project groups, all involving staff from every level of the organisation as well as service users.

A union recognition agreement keeps machinery in place for negotiations between the workforce and management on pay, terms and conditions of service and policy. A formal consultative body provides a forum for people using the services to contribute to policy development and to raise issues with management. An annual conference attended by delegates representing every constituency reviews the year's work and influences future direction. Every staff member, paid and unpaid, is entitled to regular managerial supervision, primarily a place to be well listened to, encouraged and validated. It provides a dependable, safe place to consider what's going well and what difficulties there may be, to review progress, set targets.

Here people can consider what assumptions they're making to impede their thinking, and be asked incisive questions. These are the 'what if?' questions, ones which take the thinker beyond the limiting assumptions of powerlessness to a new idea, a fresh solution, one that nobody has thought of before. Vitally, this is also an occasion to hear concretely what your line manager appreciates about you and the contribution you make to the project.

Each year everyone has an annual appraisal. This is the time to reflect on strengths, areas of difficulty, training and development needs, as well as on longer-term objectives and direction. That discussion then informs the shape of staff training and management development programmes. Every member of staff is entitled to spend one and a half hours each working week in a support activity or group of their choice. Run in parallel with the line management structure, but not as part of it, this provision of work time for personal support is tangible evidence of attention to individual needs.

To those who suggest such luxury is self-indulgent and unaffordable, I say a well-supported, motivated workforce is cost-effective. Put this provision in place, give it management backing, really make it work and you will lower your sickness, burnout and turnover rates. That makes a happier, healthier place of work for everyone and saves money. Besides, while it may not be taken up by everyone, this entitlement feeds an informal culture which is manifestly supportive. You don't have to be there very long to discover that Lighthouse is a place where people will laugh, cry and say exactly how they feel.

If people are to think well, equality must be the air we breathe. This needs an equal opportunities policy of which everyone can be proud, backed up by a strategy with clear, measurable targets for the whole organisation and for every department. At Lighthouse it means parity between paid and unpaid staff, a majority of the workforce, the subject of a later chapter. In addition, good thinking requires a *culture* of equality and of what will follow, diversity. Even though people occupy different roles at different levels in the organisation, everyone can relate as peers. If we really live it, equality brings diversity. Diversity is to be seen and heard and celebrated. It means the air is purer, the workplace safer and those who need Lighthouse, people in all their glorious diversity, will find it.

After participating in her 'Thinking Partnership' training, learning the art of asking incisive questions to remove assumptions, someone wrote recently to Nancy. 'I'd been moving towards this learning event with *very* mixed feelings,' she said, 'because of the immense blocks and challenges which I *assumed* would be too painful to release. Now I have the blocks - *true* - but I also have the tackle.' Thinking tackle. I like that.

Chapter 13
Tools for Change

This challenge of equality, of *living* it in such a way that it can take root and grow in an organisation, in our case Lighthouse, is one of those challenges which is never done, at least not until we've done with oppression. It requires constant attention, clear thinking and action.

Given our dependence for survival on a death-denying, oppressive and addictive society, organisationally we are always at risk of internalising and then playing out the irrationality, fear, prejudice, inequality and injustice we exist to challenge. It needs vigilance, as well as self-esteem, organisationally speaking, to keep the work under sufficiently close scrutiny to spot the ways, awarely or unawarely, we find ourselves participating in or at least colluding with oppression. Then, without blame or self-reproach, which doesn't move things forward and tends only to induce immobilising guilt, to think our way to active combat.

Equality of opportunity is not just a matter of policy, operational procedures and resource allocation, though all these are vital aspects of our strategy. It also involves *process*, and the quality of the environment in which the work gets done.

At one of our Friday open days, the panel was asked to share the most important thing each member had learnt through working at Lighthouse. For me, over and over again it is that solutions can be good solutions only to the extent they are good for everyone. And that they can be good for everyone only when they are the product of everyone's best thinking.

Above all, since oppression serves to disempower and silence the oppressed, our commitment to equality must include close attention to the task of ensuring that people can think well and that their voices are heard. That means everyone's voice, especially those at the margins, or who perceive themselves to be, those with least expectation that their thinking will be sought, valued and heard. 'Listen to the conversations of the world', said the French theologian Paul Tournier. 'For the most part they are conversations of the deaf.'

This is why it's routine at Lighthouse for meetings, where so much of the work is done, to begin and end with what are known as opening and closing circles. Providing an opportunity for everyone present, in turn and without interruption, to speak personally in answer to questions posed by the person leading the meeting, these circles fulfil a serious purpose. This doesn't of course mean, though, that they need always be serious in tone and content. What is something good in your life today? What are you proudest of accomplishing in your work currently? What is keeping you hopeful at the moment? On what issue is your thinking moving forward? What are you most appreciating about your team, or they about you? What is something new you are learning from someone else? What are your hopes and expectations for this meeting?

Before the formal agenda is tackled, equality is established by each person speaking, sharing positive personal or work experience, expressing hopes and objectives for the meeting, as well as being welcomed, acknowledged, and listened to with respect. Thoughtfully initiated, this process, which may take some minutes and should not be rushed, will have positive results. It will break the ice, strengthen people's connection to one another, raise the level of respectful attention, and help everyone to be fully present, undistracted and unafraid. It will increase the chances of everyone contributing, instead of the meeting being hijacked by a few who do all the talking, and of people feeling secure enough to express opinions and ask questions. It may even set the stage for the asking of *incisive* questions, the question which raises collective thinking to a new level, the question which sparks off a flash of brilliance.

It will also make it more likely that when emotions become an obstacle to thinking, this can be acknowledged and dealt with appropriately. Individuals too upset to think may be able to say so, expressing what they feel. Or the person chairing the meeting may notice that someone is distressed, and ask what's troubling them. Or, if the meeting has ground to a complete halt, it may be possible to break into pairs, simply to think out loud with the attention of one other person, or to vent feelings. I have never known this fail to restore a group to working order.

Invariably it will make the meeting more efficient in its use of time, less vulnerable to diversions caused by unexpressed dissent. It will assist the process of negotiation, conflict resolution and decision-making. Most significantly, it will improve people's capacity to think and to communicate their thinking powerfully. At the end of the meeting, a closing circle can be used to focus on people's perception of what has been accomplished in the meeting and of its value to them. Or to inspire one another in commitment to shared goals; perhaps to anticipate some specific personal pleasure ahead. Most important of all, to strike a blow against the self-doubt which lurks in all of us by appreciating one another.

All this will increase the chances of people leaving the meeting with a sense of achievement, invigorated, inspired, hopeful and well-connected to one another. Tasks to be put in hand between meetings will be undertaken easily, with successful collaboration and communication. Good outcomes of the meeting will be shared positively with others and people will anticipate the next meeting with enthusiasm rather than dread.

At the time of the Gulf War we happened to have an Iraqi manager at Lighthouse, Samia al Qadhi. She had close relatives in Iraq whom she was unable to contact. In the opening circle, at the start of our monthly two-hour meeting of senior and middle management, I mentioned the war and invited people to say whatever they wished to say about it.

Like lighting a flare, one person after another spoke at length, trying to put their feelings into words. Tears were shed, people expressed their abhorrence, fear, shame, the sheer waste of war, on and on it went. So long, in fact, that I began to be anxious about whether or not we would get through the long agenda in time. After a whole hour, it was over. Everyone round that table had spoken from their heart. No-one had been cut short.

I needn't have worried about the time. In the hour that remained we completed all the business more easily and efficiently than I remember before or since. When it was over, Samia told me that from the first hint of war, it wasn't until that meeting that she had felt really safe in this country, or able to think and function fully in her role at Lighthouse.

Next time in a meeting you're asked to introduce yourself, tell them what's good in your life too. Consider it your gift to that meeting and a blow for freedom.

Chapter 14
What Do I Really Want?

Some years ago, before London Lighthouse was up and running, I was put in touch with a man named Rory. He had been in hospital for many months with various AIDS-related illnesses. Very weak, he had now come home to his top floor flat a few streets away from my house. I went to see him and we hit it off. His partner John, who like Rory has since died too, was out at work all day, so Rory was lonely and depressed. There was nobody to cook him lunch and he felt he just hadn't the energy to cook for himself.

I managed to put together a rota of people to make sure that someone called in once during the day to prepare a meal for Rory. Since this arrangement was entirely informal and was going to stretch our resources, I suggested that we contact another organisation to see if they could send in some volunteers too. A bit dubious, Rory agreed to this proposal.

In due course someone called to assess Rory's needs and agreed to allocate two volunteers to visit him. They could start next week. Rory began to get nervous.

The day for the first visit arrived. I called round in the evening to find out how things had gone. Rory was looking thoroughly fed up. 'So how was it with the volunteers?', I asked anxiously.

'I'll be perfectly frank with you, Christopher, they were the kind of people I've been trying to avoid all my life', he said. 'They just weren't my cup of tea and I don't want to see either of them ever again.' This was bad news. What on earth could have happened?

'So what was wrong with them?', I asked. 'Put it this way,' Rory snapped, 'they're the sort that will kill me with kindness long before I die of AIDS. I really can't stand people like that. I felt utterly patronised, stifled, smothered ... in fact it was like being completely taken over.' It sounded horrible. Poor old Rory.

Now whenever I think about the implications of the Lighthouse philosophy for the nature of care and for caregivers, I always remember Rory and those volunteers. At the heart of our philosophy is the concept of empowerment. In this predicament of HIV and AIDS, we say, there is a choice: agree to be victimised or use it to grow. Either will be hard going, there is no soft option. It is hard if you let HIV confirm your powerlessness, despair, isolation and fear of being all you can be, especially if you assume that time is short. It is also hard if you seize the chance to engage your life and diagnosis with integrity.

Honesty goes hand in hand with vulnerability, walls of denial tumble down, and you find yourself aboard an emotional rollercoaster. Peaks of strength and joy, a landscape you may never have seen before, may give way abruptly to dim, damp caves of dread where meaning can be very hard to find.

Empowerment means, in essence, locating your first and final point of reference within yourself. It means deciding to live, day by day and minute by minute, in response to the simple question: 'what do I really want?'

Why is this such a penetrating, challenging, even revolutionary question for so many of us? Growing understanding of addiction, co-dependence and the abuse of children offers insight into how we may have lost track of that question, and into the behaviours we learnt as a result. These behaviours impede the struggle to be true to our beliefs and values. They disconnect us from our personal power, from a sense of belonging to the human family and from the things of the spirit. In a situation like Rory's, and in our work at Lighthouse, it is easy to see how they can compromise our aim of empowering people with HIV and AIDS, and take the work off track.

The oppressive and addictive society saw to it that many of us grew up in more or less dysfunctional families. Here we learnt to survive and to manage the unpredictable irrationality of adults by taking our cues from them, by feeling responsible for their well-being, by trying to take care of them, by denying our emotions, and by giving up our own needs and thinking as the primary point of reference. Survival in the face of violence, abuse, sexism, alcohol and drug dependency, criticism or neglect meant learning to tune in accurately to this alarming adult world, and to come up with those responses most likely to please, or at least to protect us from harm.

In the process damage was done. We will have come through this ordeal less capable of independent thought; less able to recognise that our rights and needs matter, to express emotion, to know what we really want. We may find difficulty in being open to others, especially those in authority; in saying 'no'; in negotiating effectively; and in handling conflict.

These essential tools for living will have been replaced by an addictive need for confirmation from the outside which, as with all addictions, is a need that cannot ever be filled. This damage limits our choices and functioning as adults. Programmed to meet other's needs instead of our own, even to assume that we have no needs, without knowing it we may well be trying to meet our needs, but under the guise of helping others. As a result many of us choose work in the caring professions or we become, like Rory's volunteers, informal carers. But we may, in fact, be caring for others on top of deep-seated fury at not knowing how to care for ourselves. Then, whatever our particular role may be, our care*giving* becomes care*taking*, thinking *for* rather than *with* people, unawarely making them dependent on us.

This behaviour neither models nor assists empowerment. In fact, as Rory said, it stifles, patronises and controls. Under the guise of caring, we are actually seeking a 'fix' for the craving to feel real, in charge of our lives, of significance and worth. Like all fixes, this is no replacement for a true sense of self; from this false base our caring cannot empower.

The question 'what do I really want?' pierces this deadly deception. In the workplace it is not of course a substitute for clarity about contractual obligations, roles, responsibilities, lines of accountability or professional boundaries. As on a farm these are the gates and hedges and ditches, the outward and visible means by which the terrain of work is organised to ensure productivity, the highest yield, the best return on investment. This question 'what do I really want?' is much more fundamental; it is the spring from which the water comes to irrigate the land. Without that water no growing is possible.

The oppressive society depends on addiction to stop us thinking and feeling. These are the conditions in which our effort at empowerment and social change turns in on itself at the end of the day. Co-dependence, this accommodating behaviour that derives from the loss of ourselves as the true point of reference, aids and abets addiction in all its forms, so helping to keep oppression in place.

'What do I really want?' It is a potent, highly-charged question. If asked, answered and acted upon, it is one which enables us to break out of the self-defeating cycle of powerlessness. It is also one which will help us begin to replace co-dependence (other-dependence) with healthy autonomy (independence) and a strong sense that we are 'members one of another' (inter-dependence).

Both personal and political, if asked over and over again, this question can be counted on to steer a safe passage towards true empowerment. If we really go after it, there is a fair chance it will transform our lives, our relationships, our work and ultimately the world.

What Rory really wanted was his lunch. After his disastrous encounter with the volunteers he decided to start cooking it himself. Occasionally he would invite me too.

'What do I really want?' A beautifully simple question, it is the sharpest of tools. I say, ask it; ask it; ask it.

Chapter 15
Look Up at the Stars

I f we mean what we say about empowerment at Lighthouse, then we must assume the leadership of everyone. Leadership, we say, is to do with being human, rather than with having people to lead. But what is the nature of good leadership, what does it mean to see ourselves as leaders, how can we recognise and champion leadership in others?

If you think about it, our nature is to lead. We lead our lives, making sure that things go well for us and those about us. We share who we are and what we have. We beautify the environment. We step forward for what we believe in and value. We speak up, to influence, attract, inspire. We tell the truth. We care. We love. We dream. These natural expressions of our humanity are, in fact, the foundations of real leadership.

What holds us back from building on these foundations, from assuming decisive, influential leadership in meeting this challenge of AIDS, restoring the world to equilibrium, turning our dreams into reality? What would Lighthouse be like, what might be possible, if everyone was to assume their leadership?

A glance into the Lighthouse crèche can't fail to remind us that as young people we led. We hated things to be wrong. Meghan, a 10-year-old friend of mine, loves her piano lessons. She is making good progress. Out of the blue her father, also a pianist, one day decides that now he will become Meghan's piano teacher. The lessons don't go very well. One day Meghan says, 'Daddy I don't want you to be my piano teacher any more.'

'You don't, Meghan? Why ever not?', asks her father, quite taken aback. 'Because you're my Daddy. And it isn't right for you to be my piano teacher as well as my Daddy.' Meghan shuts the piano and refuses to play one more note. Now she has a new piano teacher.

Yes, as children we wanted things to be right. We wanted harmony, co-operation, progress, respect, justice, truth, well-being. We led until we had to surrender to the incessant blows of ridicule, caution, confusion, the low sights of those influencing us. So we arrive at adulthood doubting our leadership, assuming only a chosen few can lead and setting limits on our sphere of influence in the world.

We are probably deterred too by the way we see leaders behave, lest we be thought to be presuming, or assuming a role perceived to be hurtful. The messages of oppression are further discouragement. Fine to be black, female, gay, old, differently-abled, fine as long as you agree to keep quiet, to stay in your prescribed place on the margins of society, the place where leadership is out of the question.

Wrong. The experience of oppression is the best vantage point from which to view the world, to see what's really needed, to lead. That elderly Czechoslovakian woman at the public meeting about the Lighthouse planning application probably never saw herself as a leader, nor her contribution to the meeting as an act of leadership. She is and it was.

Another meeting. A 'special meeting for worship', called by the Quakers. This happens when there is an emergency. A father has disappeared, taking his two small children and all the family's money, leaving no clue to his whereabouts. Rachel, his wife, now has £30 in the world. The police have been alerted but days have passed without any word or trace. At the meeting the mother, the father and the children are all 'held in the light' in the customary Quaker manner. Finally someone says, 'Shouldn't we be thinking about what Rachel needs?'

Silence. Suddenly up jumps Linda, someone who would never for a moment see or think of herself as a leader, or of this as an inspired act of leadership. Quietly she says, 'What Rachel needs right now is money.' A collection is made. Rachel goes home with more than enough money to meet the costs of mounting a search for her husband and children as well as for her other immediate needs.

In his Strasbourg speech about the winds of political and social change sweeping Europe another Czechoslovakian, Václav Havel, said that in managing change on this scale, our leaders will do well both to have their feet on the ground and to remember to look up at the stars. In the same way, consideration of the global impact of AIDS, and of the contribution which Lighthouse can make, brings us hard up against the need for decisive and, I believe, *inspirational* leadership.

This is not a popular idea. Fashion tends to denigrate leadership itself as a flawed concept, and charismatic leadership as especially suspect. This may be because charismatic leadership so often includes pathological elements, addiction and exploitation, as well as sparks of true inspiration. History demonstrates all too clearly the dangers of unaccountable, addictive leadership. The controlling leader out to trap followers in unthinking, unquestioning loyalty, who always requires obedient compliance. These are the leaders whose policy or organisation or movement is ultimately exposed as self-aggrandising, abusive and corrupt.

In contrast, inspirational leadership offers a steady focus on the reality of the challenge to be faced. It develops sensible policies designed with everyone's best interests in mind. It insists on engaging everyone's thinking on every issue, on championing the leadership of others, on the empowerment of each person, and on the strength of the resources to hand. Inspirational leadership points the way ahead, while pacing in step with others and knowing what's possible when. Without abdicating responsibility for taking decisions, this kind of leadership works through consultation for consent, even when complete agreement cannot be reached on the best way forward. People who lead in this way assume full accountability, within and beyond their immediate constituency.

This kind of leadership is essential. In meeting the complexity of survival issues facing the world, not least of which is AIDS, only leadership of this quality can provide that 'hope without which the people perish', and put in place the strategies we need.

In fact throughout the HIV sector there are wonderful examples of what good, committed leadership can achieve, one consequence of the issue being taken up by those most directly affected. At Lighthouse too, solid, trustworthy, but often unrecognised leadership abounds. If we are to build an organisation capable of playing its part in meeting this challenge of AIDS, then everyone must simply assume leadership, our own and one another's.

This means giving up our fear, identifying our particular sphere of influence, and coming forward to offer leadership in our own distinctive way. It will mean making sure that our leadership is never competitive or isolated, but nurtured and expanded by the most intelligent support every step of the way. It will mean relaxing enough to feel the beat of nature's pulse, to spot and tend the shoots of organic growth sprouting all round us.

And, most important, it will mean daring to infuse our leadership, not with vanity, the addictive need for control, but with the inspiration we draw from staying in touch with our hopes and dreams, with our most cherished vision for the world. With our feet on the ground, we must remember to look up at the stars.

Chapter 16
Scent of Hurled Angers

Not for the first or last time, I am under attack in the press. We've sacked someone from his post at Lighthouse, not because he is living with AIDS but because he can't or won't perform in his job. I think he's bone idle.

Our only mistake is not sacking him earlier. Everyone working at Lighthouse has to complete a six-month probationary period satisfactorily before being 'transferred to the permanent staff', as it's known. In six months it is usually clear whether or not a person can do the job for which they've been hired. But in this case, perhaps because the person is living with AIDS, we extend the probationary period. A mistake. We fail to apply the Amy Principle, so called because a friend of that name coined it. 'Ask yourself now what you will otherwise find out in a year,' she said, 'it will save so much time, heartache and probably money too.' Too true.

The aggrieved employee goes to the press saying he's been sacked because he has AIDS. He chooses his journalist well, someone with a long-held grudge against Lighthouse (a story elsewhere in the book) and gives her the names of everyone he can think of who has left Lighthouse with any kind of grievance. There aren't many but then it only takes one or two for journalists to feel entitled to write a story which reads as though what has happened in these cases in fact happens all the time. The journalist gets on the trail and stories begin appearing in the press. They make me out to be a megalomaniacal despot, an autocrat who brooks no dissent and rides roughshod over anyone who gets in my way. There is also the inference that I am guilty of misappropriating funds, making secret severance deals with staff I want to get rid of from the project.

This is upsetting even though I don't recognise myself as the person in the stories. Nor, I'm glad to say, do my staff. One group, people themselves living with HIV and AIDS, write to the press. They say I'm a person who consults widely, listens to what people think and is untraditionally accessible to my staff. I am touched.

Worried about the possible effect of all this publicity on the confidence of funders, I write round explaining my side of the story. Some people call me to commiserate or write supportive letters. Paul Boateng says, 'Never complain, never explain.' Jim Thompson, the Bishop of Bath and Wells, writes a kindly note saying what bad luck, but will I be sure to put right whatever part of the story contains a grain of truth because there's bound to be one somewhere? Sage advice.

It's time to write my next piece for *Lighthouse News*. I decide to write on the subject of dealing with attack since there seems such a lot of it about at the moment. In the car on my way to work, I am listening to Elton John singing his recent hit, 'Sacrifice'. Suddenly - not surprisingly, given the circumstances - I hear the phrase 'scent of hurled angers'. Now *that's* a good title for my article, I think to myself.

Just before the copy deadline, I call Elton's manager to check I've got the lyric right. I haven't. The line in question turns out to be 'scent of her lingers'. The article is published but now under the rather prosaic title 'In the Face of Attack'. Next time Elton John comes to Lighthouse, I tell him this story. 'Scent of hurled angers?' he says thoughtfully, 'Now *there's* a good line for a song.' Since I don't think he's used it yet, I will make it the title of this chapter.

In fact the dust settled quickly and people didn't seem unduly worried. Apart from toughening me up, the incident made me think about the dynamic of attack, by now all too familiar in the AIDS sector, and how to manage it. I also learnt the importance of offering support, not only because it's a human thing to do, but also because the repercussions of an attack are seldom confined to one individual or organisation. An attack on any one person or project is, in a way, an attack on the whole sector.

Any organisation or individual taking leadership on the issue of AIDS is wise to expect attack. This is because AIDS touches so many raw nerves and frightens people. Nothing stops us thinking so fast as fear, and not being able to think makes us feel terrible. These are ideal conditions for giving in to the urge to criticise, blame and attack, rather than facing up to the fact that we are scared, can't think straight and need support.

It is likely that an attack will have two distinct components, the particular pathology of the person or people mounting the attack, and some element of truth about something or other which the individual or organisation under attack needs to put right. It is easier to respond effectively if we can distinguish one from the other, understanding and making allowances for the pathology, and then adopting a relaxed, undefensive, open attitude to the valid criticism.

It was true that over the years we had made severance deals with a few employees at Lighthouse. Not many and not often, but a few. It isn't possible to run an organisation and never to have to put money on the table when parting company with someone in some circumstances; severance, redundancy, retirement package, call it what you will. Such settlements had never been agreed on my authority alone but, to protect us from charges of making secret deals, we did tighten up the mechanism by which such decisions get made.

The underlying pathology of the attack may include, for example, unresolved childhood trauma, internalised oppression, misinformation, denial, fear of death, confusion, resistance to change, and misdirected blame, anger or envy. All this can get acted out in any number of unpleasant ways. For example, hostility may be very personalised. This happened in a recent fight at Lighthouse over an unpopular policy; internal documents were leaked to the press and hate mail sent to members of senior management. There may be a campaign to spread misinformation, lies, rumour and innuendo. In its most extreme form an attack can of course have very serious results, destabilising or even fatally undermining the viability of a project.

However, as the Bishop rightly pointed out, the grain of truth should not be overlooked, nor the attack dismissed as simply pathological. The person concerned may well have legitimate criticisms or grievances, and may indeed have experienced harassment, mistreatment or discrimination. These charges should be heard through respectfully, investigated thoroughly and, if found to be true, corrected.

Without making a clear distinction between these two elements in an attack, we are at risk of falling victim to our own pathology. Because of our early childhood experience of criticism, most of us find it hard to stay relaxed, thinking and functioning well in the face of hostility and attack. In these circumstances we're in danger of succumbing to the temptation of retaliating, never a workable solution. Better to make immediate, friendly contact with the individual or group concerned. Then suggest a meeting to establish dialogue and try to sort things out. This will go well if we listen thoroughly to the content of what is being said, rather than being unduly upset by the manner in which it's being communicated. Even on occasions when people have refused to come to Lighthouse and meet, I have found that making direct contact quickly has taken some of the heat out of the situation.

It doesn't, of course, make sense to agree with accusations which are plainly untrue, but it works to concede whatever you can, and to make available as much accurate information as possible. It is generally true that policies and procedures are never perfect and that we can always do better, personally or organisationally. Admitting this and avoiding undue defensiveness will tend to move things forward.

It is always worth remembering too that the attack is not, in itself, necessarily an indication that either you or your project are bad. The converse is more likely to be true. If you or your project is worth attacking, it may well mean you are standing for and achieving something significant which matters deeply to people.

I don't believe we should be distracted by this phenomenon of attacks, but we should be wise to it, expect it and understand it well. Probably the best way we can protect ourselves from any lasting harm is through the pursuit of excellence in all we do. If our projects are models of openness, high standards, best practice and professional integrity, then in the end we have little to fear.

Chapter 17
Parity: Practice or Pretence?

Volunteers have been central to Lighthouse from the beginning. In fact they *were* the beginning. As Whoopi Goldberg says in one of her sketches, 'Before there was the mall, there was the ocean.' We have never lacked volunteers and it's impossible to profile them. They reflect rich diversity in their age, class, race, gender, religion, sexual identity, socio-economic and employment status. Some are HIV-positive, their volunteering essentially a self-help activity. Some have been touched personally by the epidemic, losing partners, family members, friends or colleagues. Some are retired. Some are gaining work experience leading to paid work in the voluntary sector or the caring professions. Others have no particular motive beyond the most precious of all, a simple desire to help.

Volunteers represent a majority of the workforce and they work all over the organisation, in service delivery and influencing for change activity as well as in management support. They also work at different levels, as managers of services, in supervisory roles and in direct contact with service users. Lighthouse could not function without its volunteers, their commitment and dedication are extraordinary. And thank goodness they rarely seem to leave.

In 1969, when I was first working with volunteers in London, the Aves Report made public the findings of a committee chaired by Dame Geraldine Aves. Its focus was complementary to that of the Seebohm Report, which had recommended the creation of unified local authority social services departments, but which had not addressed in any depth the role of the voluntary sector and volunteering in meeting social needs. The Aves Report made numerous recommendations about the role of volunteers, for the first time setting standards. These included the organisation of their work, recruitment and selection, preparation and training, and their relationships with professional workers, particularly in the social services.

At that time I was working for Task Force, now known as Pensioners Link. It was the vision of Anthony Steen, then a young barrister, now a Member of Parliament and also a patron of Lighthouse. It was his idea that the energy and idealism of young people, many of them still at school, could be harnessed in the care and support of isolated elderly people, sometimes through friendly visiting, sometimes through practical help like shopping, gardening and decorating. Task Force was to be a clearinghouse, drawing referrals from a wide range of agencies, matching helpers and helped.

One incident sticks in my mind. The Central Office of Information asked me to show round my local branch a party of South American politicians who were here on an official visit. As I explained the administrative procedures by which the project set up, monitored and supported volunteers in their assignments, my visitors became more and more bewildered at such formality. Coming from a society where extended family and a strong sense of community still combine to deliver care informally, it was hard for them to grasp the profoundly different circumstances of urban life in Britain, and the need for care in the community organised by specialist agencies.

But the idea of Task Force matched the optimistic mood of the time. Labour had won a decisive majority in the 1966 election and there was great momentum for change. The organisation was youthful, energetic and stylish, and we had little difficulty persuading the statutory sector to fund us and to provide free office accommodation. It chimed in with the changes recommended by Seebohm, with Aves, and with the thrust of the Newsom Report which said community service should be seen as social education and introduced into the school curriculum. Talks to schools and clubs recruited thousands of volunteers; meetings with doctors, clergy, social workers and home help organisers brought an avalanche of referrals. In no time there were ten centres across the capital, over 60 full-time paid staff employed, 10,000 volunteers on the books, and the organisation seen as a blueprint for a national scheme. In fact neither Task Force nor its national counterpart, the Young Volunteer Force Foundation, really fulfilled their early promise.

Looking back, I think a key factor was the almost total lack of attention paid to the real needs of the volunteers, or to creating an organisational culture which offered them any status, influence or role, beyond the completion of tasks dished out by the organisers. With this experience in mind, I was determined that volunteers at Lighthouse would get a better deal. Anticipating that the project would be affordable, like Task Force, only if a majority of its workforce were volunteers, I approached the challenge with my head full of questions.

How is volunteering today held back by its history? Does the historical status of the so-called 'third' sector, supplicant rather than partner in relations with the state, result in an internalised cycle of oppression within the sector? Do volunteers end up relegated to low status and influence, the least interesting work, poor terms and conditions of service? Are they in effect an underclass in this huge, vital segment of the national workforce?

With fewer in paid employment and shorter working lives, how can people's skills, idealism and goodwill be harnessed and developed through volunteering at Lighthouse? What place has volunteering in the new marketplace of the contract culture? What will be the distinct features of an organisational culture in which volunteers can make a full contribution? In a materialistic society like ours which measures a person's worth by the status and pay of their work, how can volunteering at Lighthouse be recognised for what it is, work, and volunteers be accorded their proper status and entitlement as workers?

How can reciprocity be achieved, the notion that both parties must benefit if volunteering is to work well? When volunteering is the primary, or perhaps only, formal work experience on offer, what then is the responsibility of Lighthouse to invest in the training and development of its unpaid staff? How can volunteering be brought fully into a framework of equal opportunity best practice? What are the contractual implications of bringing together the idealism of those who are straightforwardly drawn to help those affected by HIV and AIDS, with the requirement of Lighthouse for excellence, consistency of service, clear lines of communication and accountability?

It seemed to me the baseline must be the principle of *parity*, in its dictionary definition of *parallelism*, the closest you can get to equality given that this part of the workforce is unpaid. This principle is fundamental; it asserts that volunteers are entitled, except in pay, to *all* the same terms and conditions of service as paid workers. Aves had made a start, now it was time to go further.

At Lighthouse the principle of parity means volunteers' entitlement to a full range of work opportunities, to proper recruitment and induction procedures, to clear job descriptions, to managerial supervision, to training and personal support, and above all to the same say as paid staff in the affairs of the organisation. It also means they're subject to the same staff policies, including the grievance and disciplinary policy.

In order to narrow the gap between principle and practice, in 1994 we commissioned a review of the recruitment, deployment and management of volunteers at Lighthouse. We wanted to examine this principle of parity and how far we had got in putting it into practice. I had lots of questions.

What does parity mean for volunteers working anything between one four-hour shift a week and full time, alongside a unionised paid workforce working a 37.5-hour week? Where is the principle of parity in working arrangements which provide 'split' management of volunteers, part-managed by a paid volunteer co-ordinator responsible for personnel functions, and part-managed in the department in which they are deployed to work?

Are volunteers at Lighthouse in fact a disadvantaged group in the workforce? Is their entitlement accorded the same priority as paid staff who are represented by their union shop? Could or should volunteers be represented in the machinery for negotiating between management and staff? Are volunteers subtly disadvantaged in the line management structure, in managerial supervision, in consultation over policy, in training, personal development and support?

Does this then result in less, and less interesting, work opportunities? What criteria determine which posts are paid and which are not? Are all jobs open to volunteers? Are vacant paid posts scrutinised for opportunities of redescribing parts of the job, extending the range of what volunteers can contribute to the project?

This work has now been produced as *Volunteering Policy and Practice*, a kind of volunteers' charter, which sets out principles and practice governing every aspect of the deployment of volunteers at Lighthouse. It covers the full range of terms and conditions of service, including an agreement (not a contract of employment) signed by both the volunteer and a representative of Lighthouse's management.

Policies do not of course work magic. Sometimes I see paid staff assert imagined superiority over volunteers, allocating them the least interesting tasks, leaving them out of decision-making or taking them for granted. Or, in its internalised form, I hear people apologetically declare, 'Of course, I'm only a volunteer.' But now, for the first time, we have a written framework for putting this principle of parity into working practice.

To go back to Task Force and the bewilderment of my South American visitors. As we look ahead to the twenty-first century, it's no good being nostalgic for the sense of community and dependable care in hard times once found through the extended family. Our society is changing and not only the extended family, but the nuclear family as we have known it, are fast becoming structures of the past. In parallel with this change, there is now a prevailing view that we can no longer afford the welfare state as we have known it. So, if we are to remain, or perhaps become, a civilised society whose citizens get care and support at times they need it most, then into this vacuum must come something else.

Not only at Lighthouse, but up and down the land in their millions, people demonstrate their willingness as volunteers to make society work in human terms. The task for organisations working with volunteers is to create the culture and supporting structures through which that willingness can become good practice. That's where parity comes in.

Chapter 18
Remember Their Names

'**D**eath. Don't mention it,' a newspaper editor instructed his staff, 'It loses readers.' Advancing technology, consumerism, affluence and the cult of youth and beauty all combine to distract us from the stark fact of our mortality. Death, society's number one no-no. Yet we and those we love will die. 'Death the leveller' is no respecter of persons; young, old, rich, poor, famous, unknown, our time will come. We don't know how or when, but death is the only event in prospect on which we can count with certainty.

How is this denial of death played out? We don't - and don't know how to - talk about it. It's quite possible to grow up without being present at a death, the majority of which now happen in hospitals, or at a funeral. We've largely abandoned the rituals of our ancestors: viewing the dead, wakes, wearing symbols of mourning, visiting the bereaved. Funerals process through our streets unacknowledged, motorists pushing to overtake, passers-by making no gesture of respect. Coffins are carried and graves dug by professionals. Crematoria are sanitised, clocked reduction lines, coffins gliding from sight at the push of a button. Funerals are often private, brief, impersonal. The bereaved must get quickly back to normal, showing no visible sign of the loss of someone close.

As we were planning Lighthouse, Simon's mother made me think about how we might change all this. She and Simon were close and she had been spending a lot of time at his bedside in hospital. One afternoon she went out shopping for an hour or two. When she returned to the hospital she was told that, suddenly and unexpectedly, Simon had collapsed and died. No, she was told, it wasn't possible to see Simon's body. When a death is AIDS-related, it was explained, infection control procedures require the body to be placed in a body bag. The bag with Simon's body in it had now been sealed and removed. It would not be possible to see it now. Better not really, didn't she think? Too distressing. Sorry.

'I don't understand, Christopher', Simon's mother wailed. 'If I could kiss and cuddle Simon when he was *living* with AIDS, why can't I be with him now that he's dead?'

Supposing, I thought, Lighthouse could offer a *continuum* of care, before, during and after death? Supposing we had our own mortuary and viewing room so that after someone dies people could spend as long as they want with the body, in whatever way they wish? Supposing funerals could take place at Lighthouse so that people can have exactly the ceremony they want, religious or secular? Supposing Lighthouse could continue to provide support to the bereaved for as long as it's needed after a death?

So all this was built in from the beginning. Life and death go hand in hand. Candles are lit when someone dies, both a signal and a symbol. An event of significance has occurred, the dead person continues to be thought about with love and respect. Coffins come and go. Funerals are planned, in private or even over lunch in the café. Conducted in the Ian McKellen Hall, they are community events. Residents nearing their own death but for the moment bereaved can attend, staff too. Afterwards parties in the café spill into the garden. In the quiet room memorial books are lovingly inscribed.

One hot summer's day a few years ago a new ritual began, memorial quilt-making. The UK Names Project mounted a display of panels in the centre, some of them commemorating people who had died at Lighthouse. In an intensely moving event parents, partners, friends, people using the services and staff members met together to see the display, to hear the history of the AIDS memorial quilt, now made up of more than 20,000 panels, and to discuss plans to hold weekly panel-making sessions in the Ian McKellen Hall.

Words cannot describe the power of love expressed in these panels. They recall the lives, loves, and above all, the courage of those who have died of AIDS. Exquisitely, they sing of the love and pride and strength of the quilt-makers, the work finely stitched with healing found in the making. The quilt symbolises the diversity and the unity of those touched by AIDS, the human stories behind the statistics, the triumph of love and hope over suffering and loss. To be in the presence of this very personal, ordinary, yet also quite extraordinary, endeavour is to realise at once the scale and cost of the challenge we face, as well as our strength to meet it. An unequivocal statement about death, the quilt is also a celebration of life, and a work of empowerment.

This event reminded me of a discussion in the columns of another organisation's newsletter in which Lighthouse was taken to task for reinforcing an HIV=AIDS=death conspiracy in its preoccupation with death and dying. Under the chilling headline 'Deadly Counsels: The Necrophiliacs of AIDS', our commitment to challenge attitudes which deny the centrality of death and dying in life and living, and our readiness to help people anticipate and plan for death, was taken as evidence that, in fact, it's not empowerment we promote at Lighthouse, but death itself.

It's true we live in a highly medicalised society of which one product is a virulent HIV=AIDS=death conspiracy. This sets up those who are infected as doomed victims, sapping energy and will to focus on living with, rather than dying from, this virus. Despite hopeful progress in developing treatments for almost all HIV-related conditions, the failure of medical science yet to identify either vaccine or cure results in this one-dimensional perspective, willingly echoed by society and clouding the truth.

We know that living well with HIV in these circumstances is a challenge which requires the best thinking of each person across every aspect of his or her life. It is the task of Lighthouse to create an environment in which this thinking can flower, as well as one in which people can find support in putting their thinking into action. You don't have to look very far to find many shining examples of people who have dared to confront their diagnosis this way, step by step transforming their lives.

But, in addition to the conspiracy of medicalisation, we can't ignore the death-denying nature of society. This pretence that death is not the natural and healthy conclusion to life also places limits on our ability to live life to the full, to devise workable solutions to the complexity of survival issues facing us. This socialised denial of death, with the grief and fear it masks, inflicts great individual and collective damage. I think it is this conditioning, in both its personal and structural manifestations, quite as much as the other conspiracy, which disempowers people living with the virus.

Paradoxically I believe true empowerment lies along a narrow ledge, one which each of us must find for ourselves in our own way and at our own pace, perched somewhere in the gap between these two giant shibboleths, the medicalisation of health and the denial of death. Since each of us touched by HIV is struggling with the internalised effects of both, I do not for a moment imagine that, at Lighthouse or anywhere else, all of us can stay on that ledge all of the time. But if we support each other in the decision to live fully and fearlessly on the one hand, and on the other dare to face our own and one another's mortality, working through the fear and grief along the way, then I think we can trust that the work will be sound and that it will show us the way forward.

On the days when the challenge of unpicking the very fabric of our society seems overwhelming, perhaps it's worth remembering that this AIDS quilt is now too vast to be displayed in one place. And that it's made up of thousands of individual panels, each remembering a name, each celebrating a life, each a potent patchwork of love.

Death belongs to life as birth does.
The walk is in the raising of the foot
as in the laying of it down.

Rabindranath Tagore

Chapter 19
Rights for the Dying

Then Almitra spoke, saying, We would ask now of Death.

And he said:
You would know the secret of death.
But how shall you find it unless you seek it in the heart of life?
The owl whose night-bound eyes are blind unto the day cannot unveil the mystery of light.
If you would indeed behold the spirit of death, open your heart wide unto the body of life.
For life and death are one, even as the river and the sea are one.

In the depth of your hopes and desires lies your silent knowledge of the beyond;
And like seeds dreaming beneath the snow your heart dreams of spring.
Trust the dreams, for in them is hidden the gate to eternity.
Your fear of death is but the trembling of the shepherd when he stands before the king whose hand is laid upon him in honour.
Is the shepherd not joyful beneath his trembling, that he shall wear the mark of the king?
Yet is he not more mindful of his trembling?

For what is it to die but to stand naked in the wind and to melt into the sun?
And what is it to cease breathing but to free the breath from its restless tides, that it may rise and expand and seek God unencumbered?

Only when you drink from the river of silence shall you indeed sing.
And when you have reached the mountain top, then shall you begin to climb.
And when the earth shall claim your limbs, then shall you truly dance.

Even though I've spent nearly 20 years working with death and dying in one way or another, I am of course no expert. Like anyone else, I often wish death would go away, or I retreat into the numb detachment which our death-denying society makes possible, even encourages. I struggle with the puzzling ambiguities of death, always on the edge of knowing something for certain, only to find certainty slipping away into clouds of mystery.

Many writers and artists have, like Kahlil Gibran in that passage from *The Prophet*, tried to touch this mystery, this ambiguity, which surrounds death. Yet perhaps the only thing we can say for certain is that for the living death must always remain a mystery.

Until our time comes, we cannot become acquainted with it, except at a remove, as bystanders, spectators. Conditioned as we are to place high value on protecting ourselves from the unknown, on being in control of our lives, perhaps it's an affront to be reminded of death as our destiny, as we are by HIV and AIDS. It's a destiny whose nature we cannot know until we meet it for ourselves, face to face. What place for rights in the face of mystery?

While I was away writing this book, Rob Parsons, a long-serving and well-loved member of staff returned to the Lighthouse to die. For 18 years the devoted partner of Hamish MacGregor, Rob had worked first as a nurse on the Residential Unit and later, when nursing became too much, as a reception and switchboard worker. On my return to Lighthouse I went to see Rob. 'Well, Christopher,' he said, beaming at me, his eyes shining, 'I've decided it's time to die and I want to die here at the Lighthouse, my second home. We only get one shot at this, so it has to be right ... I know that here things can be exactly as they should be.'

He told me that over the next few days he was planning to celebrate an anniversary with Hamish and to say goodbye to his many friends and colleagues in turn, while he could still communicate. 'After that things must take their course and I don't want a death-bed vigil,' he said, telling me that he was making detailed plans for his funeral. Later Hamish told me that while enjoying a glass of pink champagne in our splendid Arjo bath Rob had said he had had no idea that dying could be such fun.

Once, in preparation for a speech on the right to die with dignity, I asked as many people as possible at Lighthouse what the right to die with dignity meant to them. In essence everyone had the same simple answer; dying with dignity means having informed choice about where and how to die, and choice about the people involved at the time. Many said they wanted to be free to choose not to have people around them who can't handle death. They all said that although they were users of the National Health Service for treatment, on no account would they choose to die in hospital. Significantly no-one mentioned euthanasia or assisted suicide, no-one wanted to see a change in the law as it stands, though more recently this has become the subject of considerable debate.

One person I spoke to, Alex, reminded me that he had been admitted to Lighthouse to die two and a half years earlier. Transferred from an NHS hospital his records bluntly described him as 'a very difficult patient; poor prognosis; terminal care'. He was difficult. He felt abandoned, depressed, angry and frightened. He felt his life had been wasted. After a few weeks of good nursing care, counselling and support to think, Alex decided it was not yet time to die. He must go home and get on with his life. He took up work as a volunteer at Lighthouse and lived another three years.

In this addictive, medicalised and death-denying society, we have invested the medical profession with awesome power and responsibility for our health, our survival. They, and we, feel betrayed when disease takes us beyond the resources of medical science and death cannot be prevented. Responsibility for managing the process of dying now rests with health care professionals, acute care settings the designated place for the majority to die, places where recovery, not death, is the prescribed agenda.

A former Lighthouse resident, dying in a London hospital, asked for one of our nurses to whom he had become close. She went to the bedside, joining grieving relatives while he died. Later I received a complaint from the hospital concerned that the nurse's behaviour had been 'unprofessional and inappropriate'.

The extent to which we can't handle death as a society is I believe the extent to which we also can't handle life. While we collude to deny the centrality of death, we will fail to find solutions to the complexity of dangers facing the planet. So too will we fail to understand and honour the right to die with dignity.

How can we change all this? How can we recover from the effects of this death-denying conditioning in such a way that we can create environments, at home, in the workplace and in health care settings in which dying people are empowered to live well? Then, when the time comes, to engage in the task of dying, well-informed, exercising choice, in charge of their decisions and surrounded with excellent support?

First of all we have to rediscover how to talk about death. I use the word rediscover because children do not generally find this difficult.

Rather like learning a new language, we need time and attention to peel back the layers of our own experience with death and loss, for each one of us a lifetime's worth, to come to terms with our mortality, and to reclaim our capacity for expressing emotion. We have to demystify and normalise death, yet paradoxically to let it remain a mystery also. We have to come to terms and learn to live with death, a commonplace occurrence, to give it a voice with which to communicate and express our feelings. But we must also respect it as a mystery which will unfold for each of us in its own good time and way, one thing in life we cannot expect to define, compartmentalise or control.

At an open day at Lighthouse a Swedish doctor, astonished at the ease with which issues of death and dying were addressed, asked about how staff stay motivated. Every member of the panel, including people living with AIDS, nurses and others, said essentially the same thing. At Lighthouse they are challenged to develop new skills and to give of their best; they learn to give and receive support, dealing with painful emotion especially in the face of loss. They said this isn't easy and there aren't recipes, but that above all it's this challenge, coming to terms with death and loss, which lies at the heart of empowerment.

Our many-layered approach to the building of an environment respectful of the right to die with dignity may be particular to Lighthouse. What is transferable is the attempt to challenge cultural conditioning about death in both the personal and professional domain. This has, I believe, profound potential for our collective health and well being, for social change and for the world of work.

The impact of increased 'death literacy' will be felt in the first place through changes in people, empowered in all kinds of surprising ways, taking leadership, making demands, challenging oppression and discrimination. The old, the young, the marginalised and those living with disadvantage of every kind will find their voice and claim their place.

But we shall also see the emergence of death-literate organisations. Here will be found fresh thinking about policy, provision of services and our approach to health care. The locus of power in provider/consumer relationships will shift. Change will be seen in employment rights; in the content and style of training; in more human and flexible management; in the building of durable alliances across professional boundaries. There will be a new understanding of the place of symbolism and ritual as part of the richness of life in the workplace.

It is in the interests of everyone, not least those living with HIV and AIDS, that we put death back where it belongs, in the midst of life. Understanding, promoting and honouring the right to die with dignity may well also point us to other hopeful, life-promoting ways forward for the world.

For life and death are one, even as the river and the sea are one.

Chapter 20
Things of the Spirit

We were having tea in the café at Lighthouse after an open day for the Jewish community. As she passed my table, a woman turned to me and said, 'You do know that this is a holy place, don't you?'

A holy place?

On three days each week Michael North drives me to and from the Lighthouse where he works in the Building Services team. Born and bred in our village, where he lives with his wife and three children, he works for Nancy and me on the other two days of the week. He is a tremendous friend and I enjoy the time we spend together. On the way to work at 6.25am we listen to *Prayer for the Day* on Radio 4 (I think Michael would rather we didn't but he never says so), followed by the *Today* programme. One morning it's a priest talking about peace. He ends with the prayer, 'O Lord, help us to do a work of peace this day.' 'Now don't forget to do your work of peace today, Michael', I say as we pull into the car park at Lighthouse.

Next morning it's the same priest, still talking about peace. He ends with the same prayer, 'O Lord, help us to do a work of peace this day.' 'By the way, Michael,' I say, 'what was your work of peace yesterday?' 'I haven't the foggiest,' he parries, 'but I'll tell you what my piece of work was.'

One evening as we head home I ask him about his day. After listening for a while, I ask him a question. 'Michael, tell me what it's like for you, a heterosexual countryman, coming to work at the Lighthouse, full of gay men and people who are ill?' 'There are some things you just can't explain', he replies.

'But if your life depended on explaining, what would you say about it?' He thinks for a minute or two. 'The best way I can put it, Christopher, is that it's like coming into the sunshine out of the rain.'

Lighthouse has been called a secular cathedral. Sometimes,

especially in the early morning when dawn is breaking and it's so quiet I can hear the fountain through my office window, there are moments I feel, yes, this place *is* spiritual. It's then I know the work is good. There's no explicitly religious agenda but people tell me they come looking for the things of the spirit. They come not just for the range of services but also to touch something precious, healing, life-enhancing, transforming.

One day before Lighthouse itself was built, my friend Nigel Sheldrick called at my house to see me. A member of the support network, he had come straight from hospital where he had just been given an AIDS diagnosis. He had been told he might live between one and two years more. He raged and cried and shook.

Afterwards we had lunch together. I told him I was to speak next day about HIV and AIDS at a school, and asked him what he thought was the most important thing I should say. He thought for a moment or two. Then to my astonishment he looked up and said, 'Christopher, tell them that all is well in the world. Tell them that everything is just as it should be.'

Later, just before he died, Nigel contributed to a book of theological reflections on HIV and AIDS. Writing about the challenge of facing up to an HIV-positive diagnosis, he says you have to be not only honest but also vulnerable and humble. You have to agree, as it were, to go into the Garden of Gethsemane, not once but again and again, into the despair, and terror, and rage, and sense of meaninglessness, the utter lack of certainty and even of hope.

Then, 'like entering a new doorway,' he says, 'faith emerges ... and I have sensed ... that everything is all right in the universe.' It's then he knows that life is 'chaotic yet beautiful', that he is connected with people, that they are wonderful, their pain and their hardships somehow good, their potential endless. And it's then he knows that God is alongside him in his journey, that death is the key to unlocking the vast possibilities of life. 'It seems to me that this is the essence of everything - our potential for everything amidst nothing. It's a paradox that I have to live and relive as I try to uncover what AIDS means for me.'

> The world is charged with the grandeur of God.
> It will flame out, like shining from shook foil;
> It gathers to a greatness, like the ooze of oil
> Crushed. Why do men then now not reck his rod?
> Generations have trod, have trod, have trod;
> And all is seared with trade; bleared, smeared with toil;
> And wears man's smudge and shares man's smell; the soil
> Is bare now, nor can foot feel, being shod.

And for all this, nature is never spent;
There lives the dearest freshness, deep down things;
And though the last lights off the black West went
Oh, morning, at the brown brink eastward, springs -
Because the Holy Ghost over the bent
World broods with warm breast and with ah! bright wings.

Like Nigel, Gerard Manley Hopkins, writing in the 1870s, juxtaposes the chaos of contemporary injustice, oppression, pillage of the environment and people's inhumanity, blind to the mystery of God, with the eternal spring of nature. This is 'the dearest freshness, deep down things', contemplation of which connects us with the manifestation of God's goodness and tenderness and bird-bright brilliance in the world.

I remember reading an interview with Denis Healey in *The Observer* in which he talked about Margaret Thatcher. Paying respectful tribute to her achievements, he commented that her limitation was to lack *hinterland.* I was so fascinated by his use of this word that I looked it up in the dictionary. Literally it means land lying inland from the coast, unexplored territory of the interior.

What Healey meant was that Thatcher's certainty is the product not so much of strength but of weakness, of a lack of depth and subtlety. This hinterland is found, says Healey, through literature, music, culture, a historical perspective, poetry, philosophy and spirituality. I would add, though he didn't say it, the world of our emotions and imagination. Then, a sense of mystery, wonder, the miraculous, the indefinable other, the paradox and ambiguity which lies, as Nigel tells us, right at the heart of human experience.

In this frightened society it is precisely the lack of hinterland, this tyranny of certainty, which reassures people in place of challenging their fear. At the same time it condemns us all, I believe, to endure a frightful, if affluent, poverty.

Lighthouse began with small groups of people coming together to find faith in uncertainty. They said that this crisis of AIDS is a positive opportunity, that such a place, where people can come to die, can also be focused on living well, on freedom and on the challenging of oppression. Out of this apparently ambiguous statement came a defiant and radical challenge to the medicalisation of AIDS. Now, in turn, that challenge has taken institutional form.

Microcosms of the society in which they exist, institutions are always at risk of internalising society's fear and then of expressing it in rigid certainty. Certainty, for example, about what's right, about what people want or need, about how things should be done and said, about what is and is not acceptable. Then, because we assume we know, we think *for* rather than *with* people, we *tell* rather than *listen*, we give *advice* rather than *ask*, we *do to* rather than *be with* people.

The challenge for Lighthouse, as for any institution, is to hold together two distinct elements. On the one hand, we're an institution because we've been successful; we've a job to do, a job that's worth doing well and one that requires a complex organisation. On the other hand, if we are serious in the search for the things of the spirit, for what's holy, for the transforming possibilities of AIDS, we have also to go to the hinterland, that unexplored territory of the interior. This is territory of indefinable, intangible, mysterious contours. Land of love, hope and empowerment; of managing change, loss and ambiguity; of facing isolation, injustice and inequality; of nurturing, healing and health; of death itself.

Day by day the challenge is to weave these two strands in tension, work and exploration. While doing the job, we can enter the uncertainty and the ambiguity, the state of not knowing. We can face the fear and grief and rage and desolation that comes with it. Only then can we touch 'the dearest freshness, deep down things' that will guide us, individually and collectively, to that place where 'faith emerges', wherever it may be.

The playwright Dennis Potter, facing terminal cancer, spoke on television of his approaching death:

> We forget that life can only be defined in the present tense; it is, and it is now ... and that nowness has become so vivid to me that ... I'm almost serene. I can celebrate life. Below my window ... the blossom is out in full. It's a plum tree; and instead of saying, 'Oh, that's nice blossom', looking at it through the window it is the whitest, frothiest, blossomest blossom there ever could be. And I can see it; and things are both more trivial than they ever were and more important than they ever were, and the difference between the trivial and the important doesn't seem to matter, but the nowness of everything is absolutely wondrous ...

Now *that's* a holy place.

Part 3

There's a world out there

*At some stage, said the Northern Star, you
must stop the pre-arranged reel, however
interesting it may be, however titillating to
the Gods.
Stop it and take pot luck.
Face your audience head on, without props,
without supporting cast, without rehearsal.
Throw your soul at their feet, and make them
either to trample on it, or to embrace it into
themselves.
In the waxing and waning of your tide there
is a knowledge awaiting discovery - a
knowledge never learnt, nor even sought
before because it is ... too disturbing for
humankind.
If you can find that knowledge, use it wisely
to make your world compassionate.
Use it tonight, unapologetically, before your
time runs out.*

Davison Budhoo

Chapter 21
Virtue of Necessity

L ighthouse is, of course, only one part of a much wider community response to the arrival of HIV and AIDS in the United Kingdom. While we were busy building Lighthouse, up and down the country others were busy too.

The government acted quickly to make the blood supply safe and to mount two public information campaigns. A national telephone helpline was set up. The Health Education Authority prioritised HIV and AIDS. 'Ring-fenced' government funding was set aside for research, prevention, treatment and care. An AIDS Unit was established in the Department of Health and a National AIDS Trust set up to act as the voice of the voluntary sector on matters of policy and funding. NAT's first director, Margaret Jay, was a valuable addition to the HIV/AIDS field serving with distinction in many roles, including as a member of the Lighthouse Council of Management and, later, as opposition front bench Minister for Health in the House of Lords with responsibility for the HIV/AIDS portfolio.

The voluntary sector mobilised in the fields of prevention, advocacy, support and care. The Landmark, The Sussex Beacon, Positively Women, The Globe Centre, Sanctuary, AIDS Ahead and many others; the names of projects reflect a widely-shared philosophical basis for work focused on hope and empowerment. Like Lighthouse all these projects struggled and prevailed in the challenge of mobilising their communities in support.

With the benefit of hindsight we can certainly quibble about whether enough was done, soon enough and right enough. The fact remains that now the United Kingdom has one of the lowest HIV prevalence rates in the world and a vibrant HIV voluntary sector. Known as the AIDS capital of the world, we boast some of the finest treatment centres and support services to be found anywhere.

That this voluntary sector response has been consistent with a well-established tradition of voluntary initiative in the face of newly-perceived areas of human need, makes it none the less impressive. If you were to erase the contribution of the voluntary sector from the record of the first decade of AIDS, so much of it the sheer hard work and refusal to be victimised of those most directly affected, the majority of them volunteers, our situation might now look very, very different.

What are the hallmarks of this voluntary sector contribution? What can we be proud of having accomplished so far? What were the costs? Where do we fit into a changing landscape of health and social care provision? What is our continuing role in meeting this challenge of HIV and AIDS?

If you examine more than 500 HIV-specific organisations that have sprung up over the last ten years, you will in general find that they were started by one individual, or small group of people, as a direct result of personal experience. These were people living with HIV and AIDS, or those touched personally, perhaps by the loss of someone close. The common experience for all of them, in one way or another, was a hostile social climate, leading to isolation and lack of support. It was primarily many kinds of practical, emotional and social support which people set about organising.

This brought two vital components to the work. First, a passionate commitment born of experience to the provision of services tailored to meet the real needs of those receiving them, as defined by them. Second, the direct involvement of people living with the virus, both as paid staff and volunteers, in shaping policy and in management. As Michael Callen of the New York PWA Coalition said on a visit to Lighthouse, 'People living with HIV and AIDS are the greatest natural resource in meeting this challenge.'

From our experience at Lighthouse, I know that this has not always been easy, sometimes leading to organisational turbulence and discontinuity. But it has been essential in ensuring that as organisations grew and became more formalised, their central focus has continued to be the real, rather than assumed, needs of people living with the virus.

As numbers grew this commitment to action led increasingly to a choice of services for people living with the virus, as well as to a diverse range of self-help groups. With the spread of the epidemic beyond the population groups first affected, this resulted in a higher level of accessibility to support for potential consumers. This was a human response of striking generosity. The issue attracted an army of volunteers - with a host of skills - who cared deeply that people living with this virus should have the best possible support, and who in their giving received many gifts.

The fruits of this effort are substantial. Organisations were built and funded, and the quality of life for people living with the virus, and of those involved in the work too, improved dramatically. Stories abound of the transformative experience for many people of organising in response to AIDS, of both delivering and receiving services. Stories of new levels of positive living, of the building of undreamed-of relationships, of long-postponed goals accomplished, of latent skills and hidden talents discovered, of hurts healed and of personal power reclaimed. And stories too of people being able finally to die with their lives and relationships well resolved.

It was often this voluntary effort which made an effective bridge between health and social care, in some cases developing completely new models which, while they evolved as essentially local responses, may in due course be found to have relevance beyond HIV and AIDS. But most significant of all, perhaps, is that people in these mostly volunteer-run organisations made virtue of necessity and, through caring enough to take decisive action, tackled the immobilising effects of fear, refusing to let it stand in the way of the most human response possible.

It is often said that AIDS brought out the best and the worst in society, in both a *love* and a *fear* response, two strands woven together. The contribution of the voluntary sector can certainly be seen as part of the love response, one most courageously mounted in the face of society's fear. This fear was dramatised in media sensationalism, prejudice, blatant racism and homophobia, harassment and attacks, misinformation and mistreatment, discrimination and neglect. People with HIV and AIDS often had to struggle, as they still do, without a job, a living income, decent housing or essential services. It was inevitable that sometimes this would be internalised by the groups most directly affected, acted out in a pathological disposition to play the role of victim, in gossip, attacks, rivalry and competition.

Inevitably too, this scale of response led to many people undertaking a vast burden of work with minimal resources, sometimes without the necessary managerial or organisational skills, and often without either pay or personal expenses. So fatigue and burnout, and the collapse of good ideas, even of organisations, those perennial problems in the voluntary sector, became built-in features in the world of HIV and AIDS.

As all this was happening, years of Thatcherism began to see the break-up of the old consensus about the role of social services as one strand in a comprehensive welfare state. The role of the voluntary sector, and the contribution of volunteers, had been seen traditionally as complementary. Its work was the provision of ancillary services, or the breaking of new ground, paving the way by experiment for the provision of new services required by statute. Now all that was changing. The institutions of the welfare state were increasingly seen as too cumbersome, inefficient and costly. The much-vaunted shift to 'care in the community' had coincided with the purchaser/provider split and the arrival of the contract culture. Now decisions about provision of personal services were being made in a marketplace in which, as in all markets, ethics tend to bow down before economics.

For all the rhetoric, in this new scenario what made the voluntary sector an attractive, competitive provider was value for money. Because part of our income came from non-statutory sources and we employed a vast unpaid workforce, we were seen by purchasers managing cash-limited budgets as viable providers of services under contract. All this had huge implications for the HIV/AIDS voluntary sector. Were we now at risk of becoming contracted-out servants of the state, merely doing cost-effectively - or exploitatively - what used to be done by the statutory sector? Did we risk being starved of statutory income (for the HIV voluntary sector, our main funding source) because the service-providing element in our work was seen by purchasers as low priority? Was the voluntary sector as we know it, traditionally on the leading edge of innovation and social change, under threat, our influencing for change, campaigning role no longer to be funded from the public purse?

The government began to change its tune about HIV and AIDS. Hadn't it now 'come of age' as a health issue? The 'ring fence' would be removed for treatment and care, decision-making about services devolved to the most local level. HIV and AIDS must now be 'mainstreamed', an issue to be tackled in the generic health and social care marketplace.

Perhaps it was now time for the HIV/AIDS voluntary sector to come of age too? Time to change the basis of our relationship with the statutory sector, to become partners, to professionalise, to seize the initiative as lead players in decision-making about the planning and purchasing of services? Wasn't it time to get our act together, to collaborate and to mobilise?

These are matters which would become major preoccupations for the HIV/AIDS voluntary sector in the coming years, as well as the focus of later chapters in this book. For the moment let's celebrate the achievement of the sector, and of those countless volunteers, in response to this unimaginable crisis of AIDS. Arriving as it did into our so-called advanced society, yet one so full of fear, that response was extraordinary.

People touched by AIDS insisted that not only organisations, but our institutions of health and social care, even whole communities, challenge their fear. They saw to it that policy and provision reflect personal experience and that wherever possible the most human things happened. When the history comes to be written, this effort will be a moving testament to the capacity of people in their thousands to grasp opportunity in adversity, to grow in the face of loss.

Chapter 22
Do As You Would Be Done By

Personally and professionally I have grown accustomed to attack from the gay community. When Nancy Kline and I decided to marry, there was a chorus of criticism for what was seen as a gross act of betrayal on my part.

Simon Mansfield was our first principal medical officer at Lighthouse. He was passionate that our approach should be holistic, combining high-quality medical and nursing care with the best of complementary medicine. Also a committed gay activist, he was a founder member of Gay Men Fighting AIDS and was later to die of AIDS himself. His reaction was typical. 'Simon,' I said, 'I've got something to tell you. Nancy Kline and I are going to get married.' 'Married?', Simon screamed at me, 'But Christopher, *gay men don't get married.*' 'Watch me, Simon', I replied.

Our engagement was reported in the gay press. Next week there were letters of complaint: 'get this heterosexual shit out of our newspaper'. Gossip was rife. Marriage of convenience (whatever that was supposed to mean), not a love affair. Or, Christopher Spence has never really been gay all along, it was just a device for climbing on the AIDS bandwagon and getting Lighthouse funded. Now gay men are not the funding priority they were, I was emerging in my true colours, just another bloody heterosexual. *The Pink Paper* sent a reporter to interview me. I explained that my identity as a gay man had always been as much a political statement as a definitive one about my sexuality. For me gender had been irrelevant in my decision to commit in a gay relationship, I just happened to fall in love with a man.

Twenty years later, I had fallen in love with Nancy. We had now been in a committed love relationship for seven years and, planning to spend the rest of our lives together, we wanted to marry. I couldn't quite see how this changed my identity as a gay man. Since I had lived all my adult life as a gay man, doing my bit for gay liberation and on the receiving end of my share of homophobia, I was not about to rewrite history by repudiating this. No, I would continue to identify as a proud gay man, now in love with a woman, with marriage my chosen relationship and lifestyle.

All this was too much for the reporter and he abandoned the interview. Gay men did not however abandon their preoccupation with my sexual identity and domestic arrangements. As late as 1995 the issue of our marriage was raised as an unresolved problem affecting the safety of gay men at Lighthouse. Luckily we have stalwart gay friends who are not the slightest bit confused about any of it.

My gay identity, history and politics have never been an issue for Nancy, although she does resent speculation about the nature of our marriage. Nevertheless she has borne it all with grace, clarity and good humour.

I'm with Tom Robinson:

> For twenty one years I've fought for the right
> For people to love just whoever they like.
> But the right on and righteous are out for my blood
> Now I live with a kid and the woman I love.
> If gay liberation means freedom for all
> A label is no liberation at all.
> I'm here and I'm queer and I do what I do
> I ain't gonna wear a straight jacket for you.

Right. Except that *queer* is a label too, one which, coming as it does from the heart of internalised gay oppression, is pejorative and therefore has no place in gay pride. And we have three wonderful grown-up step daughters (and a step grandson), none of whom actually lives with us.

As the epidemiology of HIV and AIDS in the UK began to change, with more infections beginning to appear in the wider population, Lighthouse, in company with other organisations, came under fire from gay activists. While most concerned to challenge the notion of AIDS as a mainly gay disease, and the description of gay men as a high-risk group, we were accused of losing touch with our gay roots and early commitment to preventing the spread of HIV within the gay community. Rather than concentrating on the rise in infections among - particularly young - gay men, we were told our education programmes and publicity campaigns over-emphasised the risk of infection to the wider population and focused instead on the increase in heterosexual transmission. It was time, our critics warned us, for close scrutiny of our priorities and spending, time for the re-gaying of AIDS.

There was clear evidence that gay men were still the group statistically most at risk in this country. The number of gay men testing HIV-positive was rising, as was the incidence of other sexually transmitted diseases, a reversal of the successes of the mid-1980s. Then the lesbian and gay communities met the challenge of HIV and AIDS, including the mounting of effective safer sex campaigns, in ways which set a standard for the rest of society, one probably unmatched anywhere in the world.

With two-thirds of new infections among gay men, it was of course right that attention to the risks of infection in other groups must not be at the expense of the campaign to alert the gay community to the current trend, and to the imperative of both promoting and practising safer sex. All HIV/AIDS organisations have a crucial part to play in fighting for the interests and lives of gay men. They must also be accountable for the way resources are used, and should therefore welcome scrutiny and consultation in order to reach this group effectively.

The majority of those using Lighthouse's services have been and remain gay men. From the start the contribution of individuals and groups in the gay community was central in enabling us to create a place of safety and to develop services. But from the beginning we set out, and have been funded by government, health and local authorities (which contribute over 70 per cent of our revenue) ever since, to provide support for *anyone* affected by HIV and AIDS. As the epidemic began to spread beyond the gay community we realised our services needed to be fully accessible to a growing number of people from other groups. Over the years we had worked at this, with the result that a wider diversity of people were now using the project. Official figures indicated that a third of all new infections in the UK were now in the heterosexual population. This had been reflected in a sharp rise in the number of women using Lighthouse, a trend we were seeing in every service.

Beyond these shores the picture was very different. Worldwide the World Health Organisation was now predicting up to 30-40 million people living with HIV/AIDS by the end of the century, the vast majority infected through heterosexual intercourse. In a world of easy travel HIV knows neither territorial nor population boundaries, and can take full advantage of poverty, endemic malnutrition, lack of education and primary health care, as well as of the turbulence of war and displacement of refugees.

Given this global picture, I believed, as I still do, that it would be dangerous to focus on who was most at risk in the UK, without clarifying that risk derives in the first place from sexual behaviour, not from membership of particular groups. Due attention to the increase in infection among gay men here, matched by proper resource allocation, must at the same time emphasise this wider context of risk to everyone.

One measure of the degree to which a society can be judged to be civilised is in its treatment of minorities. In this society gay men have not yet been accorded the same human rights and civil liberties as the majority, and gay oppression remains a daily, deadly reality. Homophobia and heterosexism, rooted in sexism and patriarchy, are deep-seated in our attitudes, customs, laws and institutions. One poll revealed that even terrorists are preferred to gay men. Yet in the context of HIV in the UK, gay men have been in the majority continuously, an unfamiliar reversal of roles. As the epidemic goes on spreading, it is reasonable to suppose that there will be scrutiny, and judgment, of the extent to which the gay community considered the widest impact of the epidemic, and was willing to offer leadership, creativity, energy, hard-won experience and campaign skills on behalf of every group affected.

My hope is that, rather than re-gaying AIDS, we shall continue to build strong alliances between all groups facing this challenge, tackling the tasks of prevention, health education, care and support together. United in the common cause of saving lives, such alliances also have the potential for changing the attitudes which underpin gay oppression, and ultimately for changing society itself. Gay oppression claims far more lives than HIV and AIDS and, in its internalised form, it keeps gay men disempowered, isolated, marginalised and silenced.

The crisis of AIDS provides an unprecedented opportunity for gay men, in this context for the first time a majority group, to reach out beyond the gay community and its particular issues, to forge new connections with other groups under threat, and to play a distinct part in creating intelligent strategies in response. Gay men can take advantage of HIV/AIDS as a vehicle for gay liberation, not by re-gaying AIDS but by becoming a model majority group, one which keeps the needs of minorities sharply in focus and acts accordingly.

I believe this approach is one which will move gay liberation forward decisively. As well as ensuring that we continue to meet the constantly-changing challenge of AIDS, building on all that has been achieved so far, it will empower gay men. Empowerment is a vital component in fighting oppression, in maintaining good health and resisting infection, and in developing the kind of leadership we so badly need for the task ahead.

Chapter 23
London-wide

The Terrence Higgins Trust was getting a bad press and Nick Partridge, THT's Chief Executive, wanted to put his side of the story. Since the problem was loss of funding resulting in redundancies at THT, Nick convened a meeting of the heads of a number of AIDS service organisations (ASOs), including Lighthouse. Nine or ten organisations were represented.

Having listened carefully to Nick's briefing, I was curious to know whether other ASOs were facing a similar crisis. Was this particular to THT, or was this a sectoral trend? I suggested that we go round the table to find out.

No other organisation was facing THT's level of crisis, but people were clearly worried about the implications for the sector of the end of 'ring-fenced' funding and what was known as the 'foster parenting' scheme. This was government funding earmarked for specific pan-London HIV/AIDS organisations, administered by the regional health authority acting as 'foster parent', responsible for making sure the money was properly spent.

Those present were also worried about how the HIV/AIDS sector would in fact fare in the marketplace of the contract culture. Would district health and local authority purchasers continue to make HIV/AIDS services a priority in the same way as before? On what criteria would decisions be made about which voluntary sector services were purchased and which not? Would the principle of 'open access' to HIV/AIDS services now be under threat? Would the threatened abolition of the regional health authorities spell significant reductions in the level of spending on the voluntary sector? How would ASOs cope with the administrative burden of negotiating small contracts with potentially numerous individual authorities?

Perhaps it was time for us to collaborate in tackling some of the challenges now coming our way? Suppose we were to set out to combat the rivalry imposed by the current funding systems? This 'divide and rule' approach to voluntary sector funding did after all produce some negative results: duplication of services, poor planning, patchy information and skills exchange, an unreasonably high ratio of bureaucrats to service workers within organisations. We all knew this meant a worse deal for the people using our services.

We agreed to meet again in a few months' time. In the meantime I investigated the UK NGO AIDS Consortium to see whether it might serve as a model for the kind of collaboration we had in mind. That Consortium had successfully brought together a number of (mostly non-HIV-specific) agencies working in the field in developing countries. It was funded through membership fees and employed an almost full-time co-ordinator, Sue Lucas. She was most helpful, making details of their structure and membership criteria available to us. This provided us with an excellent framework on which to base our London-wide collaboration.

So the Pan London HIV/AIDS Providers Consortium came into existence. I was elected chair and its first base was within Lighthouse. In due course it became formalised, with its own office in The HIV Project and a full-time worker, Lisa Power. Funded in part by health authorities and in part through membership fees, it has now grown into a network which offers a range of services to its more than 50 member organisations and which negotiates with government and statutory bodies to manage change and improve services across the capital.

There is a wide range of agencies in membership, all providing HIV-specific services across the whole of the city or a significant part of it. The Consortium includes the largest HIV charities in the country and some which are relatively small, with few paid staff or none; some are multi-service and some single-service providers; some work with everyone affected by HIV, some with targeted communities (gay men or people from black and ethnic minority communities). For some the main focus is prevention of HIV transmission, others concentrate on support services to people living with HIV and those directly affected.

This collaboration has been achieved within a system which traditionally pits voluntary organisations against one another in order to see which can provide best value for money, and one which fosters rivalry, secrecy and mistrust. Clearly it has also been the work of organisations of widely differing size (with budgets ranging from £40K to £5.5 million), with a range of philosophical and political differences, and with some existing rivalries. How have we done this?

We employed a range of strategies. We adopted a democratic structure, with annual elections of officers. We planned work which was achievable and based on areas of common concern. We avoided conflictive or controversial issues, particularly in the early days when the collaboration was still fragile. We made sure that the conduct of meetings was conducive to good thinking. Full Consortium meetings were held in the Ian McKellen Hall at Lighthouse: attended by more than 40 people, they always had well-planned agendas and included introductions, some small group work, a mutually respectful tone, plenty of laughter, breaks for networking. We aimed for positive practical outcomes, for example improvements in contracting and monitoring procedures. We paid particular attention to the needs of smaller member organisations which did not have the resources for the same level of involvement as larger ones. The Consortium was open to all levels within member organisations, including volunteers, paid staff and management committee members. We minimised the cost of the Consortium itself, encouraging maximum member involvement and ownership of the work. We avoided direct involvement in distribution of funding through the Consortium itself.

Although the Consortium was formed to make life easier for ASOs, we have found that government and other statutory bodies have come to recognise the benefits of such a move. It is easier for them to negotiate with a democratically-elected body representing all the major providers than to deal with each of us separately. Many of our suggestions for change in contracting and monitoring of services have been of direct benefit to purchasers as well as to providers. The Consortium provides a safe and structured forum for raising issues of concern to all parties.

Those with an overview of London, a city without its own government, divided up into so many separate authorities, recognise the necessity of cutting down the wasteful levels of bureaucracy which have been the result. For example, some Consortium members now have to apply to over 50 different statutory bodies to secure annual funding.

What have we actually achieved? We have persuaded the majority of statutory funders to standardise their forms and procedures so that information can be easily shared and bureaucracy reduced. We have responded to the identified training needs of our members by running a series of seminars and learning sets. We have set up a policy bank and produced a range of written policy and position papers for use by the membership. We have working groups established on contracting, lobbying, management practice and non-statutory fundraising, producing guidance on a range of areas of shared concern. We have undertaken and published an annual audit of who funds what, how and why on

HIV/AIDS in London. We have established dialogue with health and local authorities and collaborated to set up an intersectoral London Strategy Forum, potentially a pan-London planning mechanism.

Now, after three and a half years of successful collaboration, we are starting to address some of the harder questions we rightly avoided tackling at the start. These include the principles of purchasing, the rationing and merging of services, service user involvement in our organisations, why some projects collapse, how to ensure proper internal financial management and good practice, how we cost and price our services, and how, with shrinking funding, we work together to preserve services rather than preserving particular structures.

The success of these strategies is measurable by the growth in the Consortium. Also, by its recognition as the primary negotiating body for the London sector by most statutory purchasers; by its success in securing continuing statutory funding for its work programme; and by the willingness of the other sectors to participate as partners in the London Strategy Forum and other planning mechanisms.

Given that even in London, the UK's area of highest prevalence, we are facing a future of decreased funding, increased service needs, and ongoing confusion and demoralisation in the health and social services, we shall continue to need a collaborative mechanism like this one for the foreseeable future. Besides who would want to revert to our former status as rivals? We've now got to know, respect, trust and learn from one another. Because of this and of what we have already accomplished in the Consortium, we know we are in a much stronger position to face and manage change than ever before.

The Consortium has produced results which are supposed to be obtained by the imposition of a 'market' economy, greater efficiency, quality and cost-effectiveness. Yet, paradoxically, we have done this by countering such measures as collaborators and colleagues, rather than by colluding in them as rivals. 'Tis an ill wind ...

Chapter 24
If Good News Were Good News Too

'This is *not* what my readers want to read.' It was my first interview with a journalist from a sensible, mainstream newspaper. She said she wanted to do a piece on the work of London Lighthouse, at that time still only an informal support network. She came to interview me at my house. She was sneering, sceptical and hostile.

How could I possibly suggest that an HIV-positive diagnosis was not necessarily the worst thing in the world, that people in the network were hopeful about the changes they were making in their lives? What did I mean by empowerment? Was I some sort of a crackpot or something? The piece did not appear. It was that journalist who a few years later wrote those articles making me out to be a megalomaniacal despot.

Another interview, another journalist. This time a respectable Sunday newspaper. Lighthouse had by now acquired the former school and the capital programme was underway. The journalist was friendly, interested. Could she get a photograph of two people living with HIV and AIDS, standing in the derelict school? I said I would see what I could do.

Graham Gardner and Colin Clark agreed to be photographed. The shoot was arranged. The location chosen was the top floor of the old school building, where the Residential Unit would be. It was a brisk, bright autumn morning, sun was streaming in through paneless windows. Graham and Colin were wearing scarves and gloves, stamping their feet on the floor to keep warm. I could tell from her expression that the journalist thought they both looked disappointingly well. Nothing to be done about that, the photographer was snapping away. Suddenly the journalist spoke. 'Could you please stop looking so *cheerful*? AIDS is, after all, a very serious issue you know.'

In this age of information it is ironic that only bad news seems to be really good news. For a sensationalist press, apparently printing what we wish to read, the good news anticipated in a Public Health Laboratory report, that HIV might be nearing its peak in the UK and that the rate of new infections is slowing, perhaps even reaching a plateau at least for the time being, is only more bad news after all.

Without any hint of joy at lives saved, or celebration of what has been achieved, the press is laying blame for inaccurate predictions, often press-fuelled in the first place, for ill-conceived strategies and for inappropriate expenditure. As well as familiar scaremongering in most of the tabloids, HIV is now caught in a circulation war between the broadsheets.

Paradoxically alternating with alarmist stories which follow revelations of an HIV-positive health care worker, who may have died as a result of AIDS (with the ludicrous consequence that costly telephone helplines are opened to counsel those who have been unnecessarily alarmed), there is now a steady trickle of these disturbingly retrospective, wise-after-the-event, told-you-so broadsheet articles. Often tinged with homophobia or racism, drawing premature conclusions (for example about the true extent of heterosexual transmission), and pandering to what we may wish were true, that HIV poses no threat after all, these articles are dangerous.

AIDS, they say, is yesterday's scare; its days of demonic stardom are numbered; just a millennial cult of the age, it has not, after all, become the grim reaper we were told to expect. How on earth was it ever such an evil augury for the world anyway? How did the so-called AIDS Establishment dupe us all with its apocalyptic rhetoric? With only 10,000 dead in the UK, what justification can there possibly be for spending so much on so few?

As with so much reporting of AIDS, these articles are full of contradiction, parochialism, negativity and blame. They tend to distort known facts about transmission and to fudge the key issue of high-risk activity. They insist that only members of high-risk groups are really vulnerable, gay men and drug users, marginalised people whose lifestyles are to blame for the epidemic in the first place. Where does this leave women, heterosexual men, children, people from the black and ethnic minority communities, and refugees seeking asylum in this country?

Emphasising the relatively low reported numbers currently living with HIV and AIDS, they leave out those unknown numbers infected but not yet tested. They suggest that, if indeed it can any longer be considered a problem at all, AIDS may now be dismissed as an affliction of dispossessed peoples far away, just another disease of the poor. There is no mention, of course, that these people are living in places you can reach any day you choose to fly there; nor mention of the fact that across population and territorial boundaries, HIV travels too.

Whilst comparisons of spending on HIV/AIDS with that on other health issues is entirely valid, these articles never focus on the positive outcomes of the UK response, nor make the connection between our prevention campaigns and relatively low prevalence. Above all they do not represent HIV as a global epidemic, now reported in virtually every country of the world; nor do they emphasise the imperative of developing a global response through concerted international effort.

If good news were good news, what might we be reading in the press and what questions would we now be asking? First of all we would be being presented with the facts about prevalence in the UK, recognising that these are far from certain, comparing and contrasting them with our European neighbours, and asking, as other countries are, why we have been relatively successful. We would be evaluating the government's health education and prevention strategy, noting where targeting has been effective, and why. We would be identifying groups (like young gay men) which are not being reached so well, asking what we can learn from those countries which are doing better and then planning accordingly.

If good news were good news, we would be reading about the substantial advances in research, in symptom control and in treatments for opportunistic infections; about the gains in our understanding of how the immune system works, important knowledge of general relevance; and about the role of complementary therapies in an integrated programme for health. The HIV=AIDS=death conspiracy would be being challenged in articles drawing attention to the fact that people with AIDS are living longer, often enjoying extended periods of good health, particularly those who have access to centres of excellence for their care.

If good news were good news, we would be reading about the innovative models of care which have been developed by and for people living with HIV/AIDS; about how these are changing practice in the NHS and are being seen by local authorities as pilots for care in the community. We would read about how this issue has provided a context for unprecedented intersectoral collaboration, the baseline for healthy alliances in meeting the targets set out in *The Health of the Nation*.

If good news were good news, we would be celebrating real gains in sex and death literacy. We would be thankful that HIV/AIDS has exposed the inadequacy of sex education in schools, providing a long-overdue impetus for reshaping the curriculum and for piercing our death-denying culture with new understanding of human mortality. With increased awareness we would be insisting, in the name of common humanity, that people in prison have access to condoms and clean needles.

If good news were good news, we would be reading articles which challenge us always to consider HIV/AIDS in its widest, global context. Calling for debt relief, such articles would ask how the developed world can put its learning about prevention, treatment, care and support, as well as its vast resources, at the disposal of the developing world to make a real difference. With excitement, they would report and encourage examples of international partnerships and of good practice.

If only good news were indeed good news, then the press could be making a vital contribution to meeting this great challenge of our time. It could be keeping us accurately informed, inspired and hopeful that, while it is with us, AIDS may yet help unite and heal our fractured world.

Chapter 25
Tear Down the Walls

A s the 1990s got underway, there were worrying signs that HIV/AIDS might be in eclipse. In June 1993 a delegation from Lighthouse went to Berlin to attend the Ninth International Conference on AIDS. That year there were 15,000 delegates from 166 countries participating in the conference, the last to be held in Europe for a number of years, including over 3,000 people living with the virus. All week we walked the now-familiar tightrope between inspiration and despair. As always it was inspiring to see the scale and scope of the international response to the epidemic, much of it a gutsy, grassroots movement born of direct experience and nourished by a courageous refusal to be victimised.

It was this energy which radically reshaped the conference agenda. From an opening ceremony cry, 'Tear down the walls', we heard the voice of passion and authority on so many of the issues which matter most. These included prevention, poverty, debt relief, human rights, civil liberties (including freedom of travel), the distribution of drugs, resource allocation, the research agenda, the needs of women and children, gay and lesbian issues, the role of non-governmental organisations and much else.

But it was hard not to give in to cynicism and despair at the rising tide of new infections in Asia, Latin America, the Caribbean, sub-Saharan Africa, North America and throughout Europe. We heard of chilling abuses of human rights, of the executions of HIV-positive sex workers in Myanmar and gay men in Mexico. We heard of the detention in quarantine in the US navy base in Cuba of HIV-positive immigrants into the United States of America. There was predictable evidence of the continuing failure of governments to act, and of the lack of significant progress towards either vaccine or cure. With infections set to triple annually, we were told that if just $2.5 billion was spent on prevention now $90 billion could be saved by the end of the century.

Meanwhile here in the UK, the long-awaited Public Health Laboratory report had been published. As predicted, Professor Day had suggested that while the epidemic had plateaued among gay men and was declining among drug users, there was a steady increase in the number of heterosexual infections, a trend which could be expected to continue at least in the medium term.

In part at least this was good news. But coincidentally, or perhaps cynically, in that same week our government merged the Department of Health AIDS Unit into the Communicable Diseases Branch, and published a new strategy. This talked of HIV/AIDS 'coming of age' in the UK, and of the need to review policies to ensure that resources and services were being properly targeted. Then that the right balance should be struck with other health priorities, bringing the issue within the 'mainstream' of health promotion and care. Priorities were to remain prevention; treatment and care; monitoring, surveillance and research; and international action. All this sounded very sensible, but since neither the level and distribution of funding nor the specific objectives of the strategy had been spelt out in detail, we were watching developments with some anxiety.

We had recently seen the AIDS portfolio pass out of the limelight, into the hands of a health minister in the House of Lords, Baroness Cumberlege, where it has remained ever since. Then the 1993/94 AIDS Support Grant to local authorities was reduced by 19 per cent. This was followed by cuts in Section 64 funding to London Lighthouse and the Terrence Higgins Trust, whose grants were to be tapered to a ceiling of £150,000 per year, in our case half the current allocation.

Only weeks after the strategy was published, HIV was removed from the core curriculum by means of a House of Lords amendment to the Education Bill. This left schools - a key target for prevention campaigns - free to choose to ignore the issue. The move had taken the HIV/AIDS sector entirely by surprise and there had been virtually no lobbying to try and prevent the amendment being passed.

Caught between pressure from the Treasury to cut public expenditure, and from backbenchers for whom HIV/AIDS was an easy target (and one always in the aim of the reactionary press), we knew that ministers were keeping the future of ring-fenced funding under review. Confined to generalities in all areas, the strategy document alarmingly lacked any objectives at all under the heading of international action.

All this looked suspiciously like walls going up rather than coming down, and a potentially serious departure from the consensus response of the 1980s. While the notion of mainstreaming HIV/AIDS probably made sense as a long-term strategy, particularly as the epidemic spread beyond the metropolitan areas and into the wider population, I thought it vital that the change was approached strategically, with realistic timescales and funding, drawing on all that had been learnt so far and involving specialists in the field. It would, I thought, be an irresponsible, short-sighted disaster if this new direction was to be used as an excuse for winding down the response to HIV/AIDS, at the cost of more lives, or for withdrawing funds from the good work now in place, much of it pioneered in the voluntary sector. As numbers continued to rise, existing provision would all be needed, and more, as would the hard-won experience of those who had developed it.

In London the voluntary sector had by now taken an important step in forming the Pan London HIV/AIDS Providers Consortium. At this stage, there were over 40 agencies working together to tear down the walls both within and between sectors, and to manage the impact of so much change. The next step would be to develop our capacity to lobby effectively, something the luxury of ring-fenced funding had thus far protected us from having to do. We would have to sharpen our skills in communicating facts, mobilising support and fighting to ensure that good policy was backed by adequate, appropriately-aimed funding.

At Lighthouse, given the emerging contract culture, we were now anticipating that in due course we would have to increase our non-statutory income by about 20 per cent. We were concerned about how we would manage to maintain the current model and level of service provision in the coming year, let alone expand it as numbers rose.

This concern added impetus to a number of new initiatives, some of which had emerged from the previous year's Lighthouse annual conference 'HIV/AIDS: What Campaign?'. Then we had begun to consider the means by which Lighthouse could make a useful, wider contribution to meeting this challenge both nationally and internationally. A recently-completed feasibility study had indicated that a research and policy function might be one way we could provide those who speak up for the needs of people living with HIV and AIDS with authoritative data about what is going on in the field - the ammunition with which to tear down the walls. The Elton John AIDS Foundation had generously provided funding to meet the start-up costs of implementing the report's recommendations.

We had also been considering the possible implications for an HIV/AIDS-specific project like Lighthouse, and for that matter other ASOs in the field, of the government's thrust to mainstream. Could this mean diversification beyond HIV and AIDS? Could, for example, the

Lighthouse model of care be developed for other groups? If so, should Lighthouse demonstrate how, or should we provide technical assistance to others? What would be the opportunities and risks of diversification; on what terms would we consider such a move and with what focus?

Were there walls to be torn down here; walls of isolation, separatism, a need to keep HIV/AIDS special and precious? As part of this discussion, we were beginning to explore a number of new partnerships with other organisations with a view to undertaking collaborative work in the UK and internationally.

HIV and AIDS might well be in danger of eclipse. Whatever else, this next phase of the response to the epidemic looked set to be neither straightforward nor dull. But then, when was it ever so?

Chapter 26
How is Your Family?

I n this country we do not put HIV-positive people in detention (though some elements in the population might well support such a move) nor do we execute them. But this doesn't mean that human rights are not an issue here.

In 1990 on behalf of Lighthouse I had been a signatory to The UK Declaration of Rights of People with HIV and AIDS, a collaborative effort on the part of 17 agencies. This declaration (printed in full in Appendix 1) is a synthesis of the rights which the UK government has pledged to uphold for all its citizens by signing international treaties and covenants. It advocates measures to ensure that the rights of people living with HIV and AIDS are promoted and respected. It also provides a framework for raising awareness of the human rights dimension of HIV, as well as for examining and challenging discrimination.

Even though the declaration would not be enforceable in a court of law, since the UK has no written constitution or 'code of rights', it lists rights which most of us take for granted as the bulwark of our freedoms in a democratic society. These are the right to liberty and security of person; to privacy; to freedom of movement; to work; to housing, food, social security, medical assistance and welfare; to freedom from inhumane and degrading treatment; to equal protection of the law and to protection from discrimination; to marry; to found a family; to education. The initiative to publish such a declaration was taken because these rights, as they apply to UK citizens living with HIV and AIDS, were not being respected and upheld.

From the moment HIV and AIDS arrived in this country, people living with the virus had been routinely subjected to violation of these rights. The social climate was such that people known to be HIV-positive were at risk of losing their jobs, and with their jobs their income; of harassment and attacks leading to loss of housing; and of prejudice and mistreatment of all kinds in their attempts to access health and social care. HIV-positive people in prison were liable to be segregated and their HIV status made public. The list could go on and on.

In due course this work led to the setting up of the UK Forum on HIV and Human Rights, now based at Immunity Legal Centre and chaired by its director, Ceri Hutton. This brings together HIV/AIDS and human rights organisations to challenge discrimination in order to improve the lives of people living with the virus, and to enhance prevention and care strategies in the UK. It is currently applying for funding to support a programme of work on HIV-related discrimination in the UK. This will be used to establish the links between discrimination and health, to influence both policy-makers and health practitioners, and to lobby for the inclusion of HIV and AIDS in new legislation.

In August 1994 I joined others from Lighthouse and the Pan London HIV/AIDS Providers Consortium for the Tenth International Conference on AIDS, held in Yokohama, Japan. This was the first such conference in Asia, now expected to be the locus of explosive increase in HIV prevalence. In an opening address Michael Merson of WHO reported that in the previous year more people had been infected and more had died than in any previous year. Seventeen million were now living with HIV worldwide, including one million children of infected mothers. Six thousand new infections were occurring daily and WHO was predicting 40 million living with the virus by the year 2000.

In a stirring tenth anniversary speech, Dr Jonathan Mann said:

> *We witnessed the birth of an authentic impulse of solidarity, our credo was tolerance; the scope and span of our communication was breathtaking. We helped open a new era in history and as we stormed the gates of the status quo, we knew we would prevail. Just as we learn about life by living, so we have learned about HIV and AIDS through real experience, hard work, joy and pain. There is nothing peripheral or superficial about what we have done. People round the world, facing specific immediate problems with prevention and care, or struggling against exclusion and discrimination, responded with a creativity and courage which has no historical precedent, and which the world had no right to expect.*

But he went on to warn that the gap between expanding pandemic and global response was widening. In spite of heroic efforts the world over, application of traditional public health measures had not succeeded in bringing the pandemic under control. Pilot projects failed to be sustained; lessons learnt were not widely applied; political and community commitment to AIDS was at a plateau or even declining; the disparity between rich and poor, both within and between nations, was widening; and HIV remained disconnected and isolated from broader health concerns. The work of the first decade clearly demonstrated that the global strategy in its present form had become a false prophet, the source of empty reassurance and of vain hope for the future.

He said that unless we had the courage to adopt bold new strategies we risked losing the coherence, cohesion and credibility of the global fight against AIDS. In addition to traditional public health measures, these strategies must also reflect the reality of the pandemic as fundamentally a matter of human rights. We must recognise that across the world it is discrimination, the denial and abuse of human rights and civil liberties, which is the major risk factor. Then we must frame AIDS-specific programmes and services in political action to promote and protect those rights.

As 1994, the UN Year of the Family, drew to its close, the World Health Organisation adopted the family as its theme for World AIDS Day. 'AIDS and the Family' was to be the banner under which groups round the world would mobilise for a full week, drawing attention to the epidemic in every community, country and region. As with all universal themes, however, I thought it wise to approach this one with some caution. A glance at the word family in the dictionary guards against the danger of narrow definitions. Much as some might claim otherwise in order to legitimise political or religious agendas which have more to do with conditioning than with reality, the true meaning of the word embraces ties through blood, household, community, race, religion and any commonality of interest.

As 'members one of another', entitlement to the notion of family belongs equally to everyone whatever our circumstances. Just as we define ourselves through membership of the many groups that make up society, so it is for each of us to define our own authentic expression of family. Then, whatever this means in terms of kith and kin, in the true definition of the word we all belong to the family of nations now beset by the AIDS pandemic. Claiming entitlement to our particular choice of family and insisting on respect for that choice is a basic human right. Recognition of this right is vital in combating the isolation, marginalisation and discrimination which tend to go together with vulnerability to HIV and AIDS.

It seemed to me that this 1994 World AIDS Day theme, 'AIDS and the Family', should be challenging us to think about the notion of the family broadly. If we were serious about tackling the epidemic we would have to include every group where discrimination increases vulnerability to HIV, especially those which are economically disadvantaged and lack access to decent housing, clean water, education or health care, all basic human rights. We would also have to make sure the work is inclusive of gay men, lesbians, migrant workers, refugees, commercial blood donors, injecting drug users, prostitutes, prisoners and many, many others.

What might this mean in practice? In the UK it would mean the age of consent being equalised and homosexuality decriminalised; condoms available in prisons; clean needles accessible to all injecting drug users; prostitutes free to organise and associate without police harassment. The right to privacy would no longer be violated by, for example, the recording of people's possible, or assumed, HIV status on the Police National Computer, or the daubing of it on walls of prison cells. We would see health education addressing lesbians, including their reproductive needs. In every country we would see screening of the blood supply being made an absolute priority and migrant workers being accompanied by their families as of right.

If World AIDS Day could expand our definition of the family in all its diversity, then it seemed to me it would have been worthwhile. If it also spotlighted discrimination as the greatest threat to the health of the human family, and inspired us to reframe our HIV and AIDS work in the context of human rights and civil liberties, what might then be possible?

family n. *a set of parents and children, or of relations, living together or not; the members of a household, esp. parents and their children; a person's children; all the descendants of a common ancestor; a race or group of peoples from a common stock; a brotherhood of persons or nations united by political or religious ties; a group of objects distinguished by common features; a group of related genera.*

Concise Oxford Dictionary, 8th edition

Chapter 27
Wise Before His Time

Dietmar Bolle's death early in 1992 was a grievous blow to everyone in the world of HIV and AIDS, as well as to his many friends. His singular contribution merits a place in this story.

Diagnosed HIV-positive in the mid-1980s, Dietmar came to London as a refugee from his native Germany, where the social climate was chilling to calls for mandatory registration and even the tattooing of those infected. As a newly-qualified nurse, he made the courageous choice to work on Thomas Macauley Ward at St Stephen's Hospital (later renamed the Chelsea & Westminster), designated for people living with HIV and AIDS. Thus he confronted the issue professionally as well as personally, a decision typical of the uncompromising way in which he embraced his life and work until the very day he died, finally being nursed himself in that same hospital ward.

His iron determination to make a difference for people living with HIV, manifest in his wide-ranging achievements, was evidently fuelled partly by anger. He was angry about many things: the poverty in which he had grown up; his mother's early death and its impact on family life; injustice, prejudice, ignorance and the catastrophic effects of this epidemic on an already oppressed gay community; his own status as an exile for whom English was not his first language. Most of all he was angry at the way he perceived the medicalisation of HIV disempowering those living with the virus, reinforcing an HIV=AIDS=death conspiracy and setting up people as victims.

In addition to his nursing work Dietmar took up writing, speaking, training, counselling and the building of support networks for people living with HIV. He was involved with Body Positive and Positively Healthy, two organisations of which he was a founder member and later trustee, with the Nurses Support Group which he also co-founded, and towards the end of his life with CARA, an organisation challenging the institutional church on HIV/AIDS and providing pastoral care for people living with the virus. Tirelessly he advocated self-determination, self-worth and self-help as the sharpest weapons with which to meet this challenge. Modest and unassuming, he practised what he preached and inspired countless others along the way.

In 1986 Dietmar made a trip to Germany to organise the first Body Positive meetings there. This step inspired him to convene an international meeting for people with HIV and AIDS, held in London the following year and attracting 50 people from ten countries. From that first gathering has grown today's global grassroots network, GNP+, whose 1991 conference, 'From Victim to Victor: HIV and Human Rights', returned triumphantly to London, involving no fewer than 550 delegates representing 53 countries.

Dietmar knew the conference would be his swan-song and he dedicated his failing strength to its success. In his opening address he said:

> We have assisted people in Africa to build self-help groups; people in Latin America to strengthen their networks. We have brought people in Europe closer together; we have made people in India and Asia listen. This year we will make the world listen.
>
> We are the people who educate; we are the people involved in policy-making; we are the people making choices about medical treatment and care. But none of this can work when our human rights are not granted, respected or upheld. It is for this reason that we have chosen to call the conference, 'From Victim to Victor: HIV and Human Rights'.
>
> I, for one, will no longer be quiet when people in Thailand are arrested and confined because of their known or suspected HIV status; when people in India have to leave their homes because a member of the family is even thought to be HIV+; when people anywhere are tortured and imprisoned; when whole families in Arabia vanish because of a suspicion that one member is HIV+.
>
> I will not be quiet when someone in Africa is refused treatment for non-HIV conditions because they have HIV, and are left to die, their orphaned children cared for by people who themselves have HIV. I will no longer be quiet when people lose their jobs and their income, their housing and their friends. I will no longer be quiet when people are stripped of their dignity.
>
> No way. I - we - will make the world listen and make sure it hears our message loud and clear.
>
> I want this conference to end with a smile on every face. I also want it to

end with a clear statement outlining our needs, demands and desires
for a world where it will be possible to live as equal partners in every
respect. I want that statement to guide the future work of our
international network.

It did. As project chair, Dietmar watched his vision of a worldwide
network of self-help win recognition (and funding) from international,
governmental and national agencies. He saw GNP+ begin to flex its
muscles in speaking out against abuses of human rights and civil liberties,
set an agenda for action, and mandate a newly-elected steering
committee to establish a permanent framework to maintain momentum
between annual conferences.

That so much should be achieved by a young man living alone,
with a life-threatening diagnosis, in failing health and far from home, is
extraordinary.

The secretariat for the London conference was based at
Lighthouse, so I was privileged to work alongside Dietmar through the
months before and after the event. Having known each other only
slightly over the years, during those hectic months we became real
friends and I had the joy of discovering the private person behind the
public activist. He was an unapologetic foodie and we would go out for
leisurely meals in his favourite restaurants. He loved the countryside,
coming to stay in Oxfordshire (where he planted a wych-hazel in the
garden) and enjoying long walks along the banks of the Thames.

Dietmar knew that social action and personal growth are both
essential components of world change if it is to stay on course and bear
fruit. As spiritual as he was political, he attended to the journey of the
soul in tandem with his activism, also sustaining a rigorous commitment
to his own psychoanalysis.

His home, a garret flat in west London he called The German
Cottage, was the sanctuary to which he would retreat to keep his journal,
compose poetry and create fairy stories inspired by his love of nursery
rhymes, children's books and Norse mythology. Here he collaborated
with Ann Richardson on a collection of personal stories, *Wise Before Their*
Time: People Living with HIV and AIDS, published by HarperCollins.
Among his few worldly goods, he was proud of a late love affair with
painting, which produced bold abstracts rich in colour and vitality.

It was particularly in this private domain that Dietmar found the
strength to meet the incessant and changing demands of his work, and to
overcome all manner of obstacles including at times fierce criticism and
attack. Formidably intelligent and entirely his own man, he could be

difficult and obstinate, often riding roughshod over others. Equally he could quickly rethink his position, conceding a point with grace and courtesy.

Angular in his dealings with people, he was at a loss when things went too smoothly. He was most comfortable wrestling with life, then regaling his friends with its hardships. He had little personal ambition or vanity, yet craved recognition for his achievements. He could easily feel injured as, for example, when GNP+'s new international steering committee only grudgingly bestowed on him the emeritus membership which was his due.

Always lonely, he was mistrustful of intimacy and often disappointed in love. Yet, secure in his identity as a gay man, he respected other people's choices and enjoyed a wide diversity of friendships, especially with women. Ruthlessly honest with himself, he was perceptive about others and he could sometimes be very harsh in his judgments. Yet he was also witty and forgiving, capable of great generosity and tenderness, and a giver of the most imaginative gifts.

> *Through the night of doubt and sorrow,*
> *Onward goes the pilgrim band,*
> *Singing songs of expectation,*
> *Marching to the promised land.*

Pilgrim and warrior, Dietmar's courageous march was done.

He was a man of goodness and decency. He was also an outstanding example of empowerment. His legacy is a vibrant worldwide network of people supporting one another in refusing to be victimised, in making the most of life and in taking leadership in the face of HIV and AIDS.

In 1995 GNP+ held its seventh international conference in Cape Town, South Africa, where the focus was human rights. Reflecting a new level of universality and diversity, it was attended by 800 delegates representing 82 countries. Dietmar Bolle would have been quietly proud.

Chapter 28
Who Pays the Piper, Who Calls the Tune?

By the mid-1990s the UK voluntary sector was playing its part in response to HIV and AIDS against a background of sweeping change. Whether they wanted to or not, organisations were having to take account of new legislation and financial arrangements, in particular the new world of the market. This meant new ways of working. Needs assessment must be up-to-date and based on accurate data. Services must be tailored to match purchasing priorities. Planning cycles must fit in with health and local authority decision-making. Contracts must be negotiated and monitored.

Commissioners were increasingly interested in targets, quality indicators and measurable 'outcomes'. A new level of professionalism and accountability was required. People began to worry that the distinct characteristics of the voluntary sector were now under threat. The 1990 NHS and Community Care Act had formed the basis of recent reforms, bringing about the purchaser/provider split and ushering in the contract culture. It also introduced the transfer of funds from the Department of Social Security to local authorities, care management arrangements and more contracting-out to the independent sector. The 1989 Children Act called for innovative, family-centred provision for children, a group increasingly affected by HIV.

There was a steady stream of government edicts too. A new strategy document announced the end of ring-fenced funding for care, and the thrust towards the mainstreaming of HIV and AIDS. *Health of the Nation* identified HIV/AIDS as a priority and promoted 'healthy alliance' working. The Tomlinson Report recommended a shift away from hospital services towards community-based care, presaging a reduction in the number of acute hospital beds in London. The NHS itself was restructured, yet again, with the number of regional health authorities being reduced prior to their abolition entirely by 1996. Decision-making and purchasing budgets were devolved to district health authorities.

Lighthouse was luckier than some organisations. Although our Department of Health Section 64 funding allocation was tapering annually (to half its original size) and our London Boroughs Grants Committee grant was (temporarily) reduced, the 'foster parenting' scheme was replaced by 'host purchasing' arrangements with the new Kensington & Chelsea & Westminster Health Commissioning Agency. In effect this meant that we would not move fully into the competitive market until 1996.

All these changes were certainly putting the voluntary sector on a steep learning curve. New skills were required. Corporate planning became an essential framework for decision-making. Quality, efficiency and cost-effectiveness were the new watch-words. But did all this really constitute a threat to the traditional identity of the sector? And what was this cherished tradition anyway?

When I was first working in the voluntary sector in the 1960s, a national committee was set up to examine the role of volunteers in meeting social needs. The report which followed, *The Voluntary Worker in the Social Services* (always known as the Aves Report after the committee's formidable chair Dame Geraldine Aves), made numerous recommendations, for the first time setting standards. It also proposed that a new national organisation be set up to serve as a focus for the work of volunteers. The Volunteer Centre UK was duly established and in 1976, two or three years later, I answered an advertisement for the vacant post of director. To my alarm I was informed that the first stage of the interview process was to be a private meeting with Dame Geraldine Aves at her flat in Highgate. No equal opportunity process this, obviously I was to be vetted.

My recollection is that the interview was brief and blistering. With the good judgment on which she prided herself, Dame Geraldine quickly consigned my application to the bin. I was left with the general impression that I ought to be thoroughly ashamed of myself for the presumption that my slender experience as director of one small London voluntary organisation, no matter how successful it might have been in capturing headlines and attracting volunteers, could in any way have equipped me for the post at The Volunteer Centre. It was a most inglorious encounter and it may be no coincidence that I've never actually applied for a job since.

After Dame Geraldine's death, The Volunteer Centre instituted an annual lecture in her memory. In 1993 I was invited to deliver that lecture, choosing the title 'The World of Work is Changing - Volunteering into the 21st Century'. Nearly 30 years on, as this century draws to its close, this was an opportunity to reflect on the future of the voluntary sector and of volunteering, an activity in which Dame Geraldine believed passionately, in a social landscape changed so dramatically by 14 years of Thatcherism.

Then there was broad consensus about the role of a comprehensive, cradle to grave, welfare state. The role of the voluntary sector, and the contribution of volunteers, was seen as complementary. Our work was the provision of ancillary services, either services which could not be provided by the state or services breaking new ground by experiment, demonstrating a need which would in due course be met by additional statutory provision. Now things look very different. Not only is such a welfare state increasingly seen as unaffordable, there is also recognition that the independent sector can fulfil certain functions much better than the state.

Tradition is of course a two-edged knife in the shaping of our structures of care. For the voluntary sector in Britain tradition brings with it accumulated wisdom gleaned from experience. It offers people who have a vision of change well-tried, flexible formulas. It allows new and sometimes frightening issues, as in the case of HIV and AIDS, to be brought powerfully, imaginatively and swiftly to public attention, as well as to the public purse, much faster than through the corridors of power. This is one aspect of Lighthouse most frequently commented on by statutory observers, that it had a lead time from inception to completion of a £4.5 million capital project of only 22 months. This, they say, could never have happened in the statutory sector where decision-making is subject to so many layers of scrutiny and is therefore a much slower process.

But this tradition has its roots in old-fashioned, middle-class paternalism, and in a period when those who had more than enough expiated a little guilt by spending some of their surplus money and time on the needy. It was called *charity*, just as our organisations are today. The work was not funded from the public purse, nor attentive to issues of rights, social justice or equality of opportunity. Nor was there generally volunteer or consumer involvement in policy and management.

Framed in the traditional prescription for charitable bodies is the principle that they should not engage in political activity. Ambiguously, while so many organisations exist to address social issues all too obviously overlooked by the framework of care created by statute, and are depended on for a vast array of essential services, they are supposed to refrain from overtly political action to change the very conditions which necessitated their creation in the first place. In 1995, I am glad to say, the Charity Commission published new guidelines which go some way to legitimising political campaigning by charities, provided the campaign relates directly to the charity's main object. A recent Home Office-funded report on charities, however, reinforced this principle by suggesting that only service-providing organisations should be eligible for public funds. Those involved in campaigning, it suggested, should fend for themselves. This overlooks the reality, certainly true of HIV and AIDS, that most voluntary organisations are engaged in both providing and campaigning, each strand of activity informing and strengthening the other. Although ministers were swift to distance themselves from the report, it did reveal a worrying undercurrent.

Words have interesting connotations. For example the word *voluntary* implies non-contractual, optional, discretional, amateur, supernumerary, and therefore of course dispensable. On the other hand the word *statutory* implies mandatory, requisite, necessary, essential, professional, and therefore of primary importance. This is not mere pedantry. The real meaning of words gets internalised and then expressed in structures, attitudes, behaviour and working practice.

Even though the voluntary sector demonstrates the essential nature, effectiveness and value-for-money of what we do, because the work is largely undertaken by volunteers, at the funding table the history and perceived status of the sector in practice makes us supplicants rather than partners. In that role we are then vulnerable to the variable priorities, prejudices and whims of statutory purchasers. We often under-price our services, in turn agreeing to be under-resourced and funded retrospectively, or at such short notice that responsible financial management and strategic planning is a practical impossibility. This leads to crisis management, unstable organisations, poor terms and conditions of service, a demoralised workforce of paid workers and volunteers and, in the end, to poor work.

This cycle of oppression and inequality is then internalised and played out within the voluntary sector, both between organisations and within the workforce. Organisations will tend toward isolationism, to defensiveness, to lack of mutual respect and co-operation. Rivalry, gossip and attacks are common. Preserving organisations becomes more important than preserving services. Fierce competition for funding, and sometimes for the loyalty of the consumer group, comes before collaboration. Within organisations this gets played out in a pecking order of hierarchy and the relegation of volunteers to the bottom of the heap, the place of least influence.

Of course none of this makes good sense. These characteristics of the voluntary sector are ones which I hope these changes may provide us with an opportunity to grow out of and shed. It is in the interests of consumers of services and of all those engaged in planning, funding and providing them, as well as of the wider community in which we work, that a new style of partnership be developed between the sectors.

This partnership must be one in which the voluntary sector takes its place as a professional, well-treated and respected equal, with shared decision-making matched by mutual accountability. I think such partnerships are possible without threat to our independence; they may even in the course of time strengthen it by virtue of replacing an adversarial relationship with a collaborative one. Within these partnerships the voluntary sector will also, if anything, be better placed to speak up with authority for the needs of people living with HIV and AIDS and to bring influence to bear on statutory decision-making.

People's worries in the face of rapid change are understandable. But I believe the current demands on the voluntary sector represent opportunity much more than threat. They provide the opportunity to let go some constraints inherited from the past, to sharpen both the performance and image of our sector, equipping ourselves as first-class providers of essential services. In the process we shall earn our rightful place as partners in the challenge of shaping viable structures for care in the twenty-first century.

Chapter 29
Paris

In 1988, the year the Lighthouse building was opened, I wrote a commemorative essay. This is how I began:

Calamity of every kind - war, famine, pestilence, catastrophe, injustice, oppression and natural disaster - is, historically speaking, routine in human experience, much as we in the rich nations of the so-called first world like to pretend otherwise. And routinely we respond, conservatively, piecemeal and often very late in the day.

We congratulate ourselves for not throwing money at problems. We investigate, report, recommend, legislate, raise standards, develop technologies, reorganise and restructure. But all too often we continue substantially as before, until calamity takes us by surprise once more.

Yet history also shows that, from time to time, the human race is confronted by crises which impact in a quite different, profound and transforming way, the repercussions sounding across every boundary and population, as well as on the pattern of life for future generations. These are the events which bring unimaginable crisis and great challenge; events that expose the fabric of society where it is worn out or rotten through and through, and in doing so, stir the human spirit out of its habitual complacency to insist on, and fight for, a response focused on fundamental and far-reaching change.

I believe that in our time AIDS is such an event and that history will judge this generation by the quality of our response.

The longer-term dimensions of the pandemic cannot yet be forecast with complete confidence or accuracy. Much depends on the success of our strategies in the next period. Based on the lower limit of World Health Organisation predictions for each region, cautious estimates project by the year 2000 a cumulative total of 30–40 million infections in men, women and children. More than 90 per cent will be in developing countries, with a total of close to 10 million adults living with AIDS. In Africa AIDS has tripled an adult mortality rate already eight times that in the developed world. By 2000 the cumulative total of HIV-related deaths worldwide is predicted to rise from its current total of two million to eight million.

Projections of the number of infants and children with AIDS are based on perinatal transmission rates of about 30 per cent. However, because infected mothers are likely to die within 5–10 years after giving birth, uninfected infants will constitute a growing population of orphans, possibly as many as five million by 2000. This figure will increase again as a result of the deaths of mothers infected in the 1990s.

As the epidemic ages in some parts of the world and the pool of non-infected sexually active adults at risk of HIV infection decreases, large numbers of young people becoming sexually active will replenish the pool of susceptible people, especially in developing countries. The proportion of new infections in young people is therefore likely to increase with time. Evidence of high incidence rates in young age groups is now emerging from various countries. In the USA the number of those aged 13 to 21 infected with HIV rose by 77 per cent between 1991 and 1993. This highlights the vital role of prevention programmes to target young people at a very early age. The fact that in the UK we have the highest teenage pregnancy rate in western Europe should give us no grounds for complacency.

It is clear that the pattern of explosive growth in new HIV infections which occurred in much of the world through the 1980s, is set to be tragically repeated in many parts of Asia through the 1990s. While India and Thailand still account for the majority of infections, we have seen significant levels of HIV in China, Vietnam, Cambodia, Malaysia and elsewhere. In much of eastern Europe, particularly in the countries of the former Soviet Union, there is a sexual revolution underway reminiscent of what happened in western Europe in the 1960s, but with woefully inadequate sex education and prevention programmes. Here the magnitude of the epidemic is still poorly defined but must be expected to be very serious. In addition, the pandemic will persist throughout the world where it is already established, especially in developing countries, as susceptible populations are replenished by younger generations.

In the face of this grim picture what, eight years on, can we now say about the quality of our response? Given the simplicity of the facts about transmission, the extreme fragility of the virus, and thus the sheer preventability of this global disaster, how on earth, we may well ask, could we ever have let this happen?

What has been achieved by the public health response so far and what has it taught us about what should be done in those countries where the epidemic is still expanding but not yet fully visible, as well as in those where it is well established? What now needs to happen if we are to intervene to alter the course of this monster ravaging the globe?

The first global strategy, based on what was known at the time both about AIDS and about public health, concentrated on prevention strategies aimed at changes in personal behaviour, since this was how the virus was spreading. Programmes were based on a three-part model, two parts deriving from traditional public health practice and one part breaking new ground. The two standard parts of this 'prevention triad' were information and education, and health and social services. The third part, not traditionally part of the public health lexicon, was recognition of the need to prevent discrimination of people living with the virus.

The first period of global mobilisation from 1986 to 1989, possibly the swiftest public health response in history, had two elements. First, countries and communities were mobilised to create programmes which could deliver this 'prevention triad'. Second, a powerful set of ideas about the meaning of the pandemic was expressed as global policy.

HIV was the first pandemic to be identified as both a scientific and a societal challenge. The narrow biomedical paradigm of the disease was broadened to include its societal impact and meaning; and a global strategy developed which respected and fostered diversity, yet recognised common ground in local, national and international efforts. While this was good public health built to modern specifications, it was still only an improved, global expression of that traditional public health paradigm. For this reason, paradoxically, while the collective work during this period was undoubtedly successful in slowing the spread of HIV, it was also woefully inadequate, as current global prevalence confirms.

It is now clear that the first global AIDS strategy, while it was necessary, innovative and courageous, the best we could do in the circumstances, did not bring the pandemic under control. In fact, if countries so far relatively less affected, like for example Indonesia, adopt the components of the present strategy, it is likely to have little impact on the shape of the coming epidemic. Something radically different is now required.

Public health has long recognised the importance of societal factors for health. But there is a gap between recognition and response.

We see but we don't act. The gap between our understanding of the underlying causes of ill health and the scope of most public health activity yawns. It shows the extent to which we tend to defer, as if it was natural and right and just, to political, economic, cultural or social reasons why some sensible health goal can be dismissed as impractical or impossible.

Perhaps AIDS at last presents us with the opportunity, I would say the imperative, of turning this received wisdom on its head and of uprooting this pandemic by tackling its deeper, underlying roots. We have seen the pandemic follow the path of least resistance in every society; specific to that society, yet remarkably similar round the world. The major societal risk factor for vulnerability to HIV is to belong, before HIV ever came on the scene, to any group which is discriminated against. Discrimination takes many forms, structural, social, personal, and results in people being marginalised, stigmatised and in some way excluded from society. Most often this discrimination will be on the grounds of socio-economic status, race, gender, ethnicity, religion, age or sexual preference.

Here in the UK, HIV has struck hardest at people from groups already traditionally marginalised, in particular gay men, drug users and people from black and ethnic minority communities. There is an established media notion of 'innocent' and 'guilty' people living with HIV, all too clearly rooted in prejudice. HIV is an unpopular cause, misrepresented as over-funded and somehow sustained by celebrity funders, media coverage promoting the belief that HIV-positive people have somehow brought it upon themselves.

All over the world the picture is the same. The path of the pandemic shows us all too clearly that wherever there is discrimination, there is increased vulnerability to HIV. Ergo, we have to recognise discrimination, the denial and abuse of human rights and civil liberties, not just as a consequence of HIV, but as an underlying cause of the pandemic. Then we have to design brand new strategies which focus on protecting and promoting those rights.

Cut to Paris, France. World AIDS Day, 1 December 1994. Heads or very senior members of the governments of 42 nations, with representatives of the HIV/AIDS sector and people living with the virus in attendance, are convening for a summit organised by the World Health Organisation and hosted in the UNESCO building. The UK delegation is led by the Secretary of State for Health, Virginia Bottomley. The voluntary sector is represented by Nick Partridge of the Terrence Higgins Trust and by Joan Fratter of Barnardo's. Sue Lucas of the UK NGO AIDS Consortium and Jo Manchester of the International Community of Women are also present.

Diplomatic courtesies are exchanged, the pecking order fussed over, a long lunch break taken (heads of delegations being whisked away to a nearby palace), and ministerial speeches delivered. Virginia Bottomley makes a speech in which she attributes the UK's success to collaboration between government and the voluntary sector, especially to 'the enlightened attitude of those most at risk'. She also announces an additional £2 million over three years to be spent on HIV/AIDS research through the Overseas Development Administration, emphasising the government's commitment to partnership at the international level.

As all good summits should, the proceedings conclude with a declaration, written ahead of time and informed by the work of numerous pre-meetings, and duly signed by the heads of delegations in turn throughout the day. That declaration is summarised in chapter 35 and printed in full in Appendix 2. Its scope is much, much more far-reaching than I had dared hope. For the first time, we have a framework for tackling the pandemic as an issue both of health and human rights. It's a big step forward. The challenge now is to turn the summit's raft of concrete undertakings and resolutions into imaginative, collaborative strategies for action.

There is much to do; there is not much time; we must go slowly.

Chapter 30
Companions in Dance

Words, like issues, come and go. Their real meaning, if ever fully comprehended, changes or gets lost with use and with the passage of time. Much in vogue in the world of HIV and AIDS these days, partnership is one such word.

Literally meaning a framework for sharing risks and profits, companions in dance, associated players in the same game, all images redolent with equality, it is a word which slips easily from the lips and pens of those with power and resources to hand. It is a word liberally scattered over documents which, week in, week out, cascade onto my desk. It is there in the Paris Declaration, 'in a spirit of true partnership'. It is also a word I have used in this book. But in the context of AIDS, what does it really mean?

Towards the end of 1994 Lighthouse hosted the launch of Simon Garfield's award-winning book, *The End of Innocence: Britain in the Time of AIDS*. Its appearance reminded us that over a decade of grinding work and escalating loss is now history. And with the writing of history comes judgment. Garfield's account of how individuals, institutions and systems coped with the crisis makes sober reading. Woven with the facts about policy and funding, the heroism, drive and innovation so characteristic of the response to AIDS is recalled. But so is a fantastic tale of struggle against the odds, of prejudice, panic, hysteria, of professional rivalry, political in-fighting and crisis management.

Not much about partnership here. As an interim judgment, the book's bottom line is clear: 'could do better, must try harder'. Now well into its second decade and deemed by government to have come of age as a health issue, the UK epidemic at least, Garfield suggests, is at a crossroads and the voluntary sector in danger of losing its way.

Will we learn the lessons of the first decade? Given the emphasis on mainstreaming is there the political will to apply them? In the new world of contracts and care in the community, will HIV/AIDS services continue to be a purchasing priority? Can the HIV/AIDS sector work with, contribute to and learn from the generic voluntary sector? What will it take to build on the UK's success in keeping HIV prevalence low and in developing innovative models of care, with the voice of people living with the virus influential in the design and delivery of services? With a shrinking statutory funding base, can a restructured voluntary sector, leaner, fitter, more professional, continue to reach the most vulnerable and marginalised groups? Importantly, not least in the light of the Paris Declaration, I would ask another question: what role for the UK voluntary sector, with its track record of success in community mobilisation, in hope and empowerment, in the global picture?

We will have to search for the answers to these questions, ones which every HIV/AIDS organisation must confront in the next period, if we're to move forward in the UK, let alone close that ever-widening gap between the pandemic and the global response. But I think it's through developing our understanding of this notion of partnership, and through active commitment to building partnerships, that most likely those answers will be found.

Looking back over ten years of building and developing Lighthouse, I can see that this theme of partnership has been central all along. To the extent that we've been successful, the secret lies in our pursuit of partnership, both within and beyond the project, in seeking and promoting co-operation, collaboration, rather than competition and rivalry.

In our infant years such was the pressure to get the model of care up and running, that it took a little while to recognise this fully and to devise strategies accordingly. In 1992 our annual conference title was 'HIV/AIDS: What Campaign?', an attempt to unravel the various overlapping campaign issues contained within the epidemic. We heard remarkable speeches by Dr James Tumwine from Uganda, Dr Radium Bhattacharya from India, Nancy Gochoka from Kenya and Lisa Power from the UK, later to our good fortune to become co-ordinator of the Pan London HIV/AIDS Providers Consortium. Always respectful and in turn funny, moving and inspiring, each challenged our ignorance, parochialism and complacency. They urged us to face the explosively political nature of HIV and AIDS, to build on our considerable experience to understand and identify with the various campaign issues, and to make our voice heard, always working in partnership with other groups, nationally and internationally.

This was our fifth annual conference and one I look back on as a landmark in the project's development. The first three conferences were preoccupied with domestic issues, with resolving tensions caused by such rapid growth, both in the project and in the epidemic, as well as by our still dim understanding of this notion of partnership. In turn we struggled with what partnership might mean between the early pioneers and the first professional staff. Then between those who use the services and those who provide them, including those who cope with the ambiguity of belonging in both camps. Next between a diversity of groups needing access to services. And finally between paid workers, a minority, and the substantial majority of our workforce, the volunteers on whom the success of the project hinges. To each of these potentially conflictful challenges we applied exhaustively the thinking environment principles outlined in chapters 12 and 13, thinking our way to solutions that would work in everyone's best interests.

By 1990 we were sufficiently confident in the strength of the partnership developing between groups within Lighthouse, assisted by improved policies, a consultative framework, a divisional structure and a union recognition agreement, to look forward. We drew up a five-year plan laying the foundations for operational consolidation, for developing Lighthouse as a centre of excellence, and for disseminating its values, knowledge and good practice through education, training and consultancy in this country and beyond.

There was agreement that outreach, rather than replication, would be the means by which we could best contribute to meeting the needs of people living with the virus wherever they may be. We recognised that long-term this will not be by proliferating HIV/AIDS-specific projects, but by working in partnership wherever we can to raise awareness, to support the development of provision which meets the needs of affected populations, as defined by them, and to promote services focused on empowerment.

In 1991 for the first time we used the conference to look beyond the project. We considered whether and how our work was making an impact on the wider community and at where we needed to be building partnerships, with a wider diversity of people with HIV and AIDS, as well as with a range of different services and professions. A commitment to increase the accessibility of our services, all of which were being stretched to capacity, meant outreach work, consultation, policy development, and scrutiny of the sensitivity of each service, and of the project as a whole, to the particular needs of each group. In the shift from demand-led to planned services, workloads were gauged to allow time for work in partnership with many other agencies, as well as for representational work on policy and planning groups, at conferences, seminars and many other kinds of meetings.

During that year Lighthouse played a lead role in establishing the

Pan London HIV/AIDS Providers Consortium described in chapter 23. This was a vital partnership for the HIV/AIDS sector in London, providing for the first time a forum for the collective voice of providers, as well as for dialogue with health and local authority purchasers and with government.

That year too we commissioned a study to help us begin to formulate a strategy for developing international partnerships. This resulted in the decision to set up a research and policy function within Lighthouse, enabling us to speak up for the needs of people with HIV and AIDS with more authority. We also framed clear criteria for evaluating opportunities to work internationally, based on the principle that such work must focus on the development of mutually beneficial partnerships, as well as being culturally appropriate and sustainable. There has followed a range of undertakings in partnership with HIV/AIDS organisations in India, the Caribbean, France and Russia, as well as a vast amount of informal collaboration with people in the field all over the world.

The interplay between these various strands of Lighthouse's local, regional, national and international work to put its vision in practice is the subject of the next part of this book, explored through the life and work and death of Derek Fraser, someone who would have considered himself a most unlikely hero.

And the future? Addressing women at the end of her book *Women and Power: How Far Can We Go?*, Nancy Kline says:

> *In this next thrust of change we must remain firm and determined, but we must also ... go 'where the dancing is'.*
>
> *This approach is one which must include everyone, where we think afresh together at the same time as marching side by side, where we take the time each day to recognise and remove internal barriers so that we can permanently topple the external ones. In this 'dance' joy is not poisoned by fury; we will not think as sophisticated victims but as powerful inventors; we can withdraw from the sexism around us while drawing out the best in each other; and women and men can think together instead of abandoning each other in anger and disappointment. We may eventually be able to step out of the cycles of history that return us to the same old problems era after era if we can learn now to think together as in a dance.*
>
> *Our dreams for change are big. Our strategies must be big, too.*
>
> *As we link our minds, we have to know exactly where we are and sense what the next step will be together. We have to respond*

accurately to the lives of those around us. We will turn quickly sometimes, lean gently sometimes, pause sometimes and reach out or draw in at just the right moments to stay true to our beat and to avoid obstructing the paths of others as we go. We must listen for the music, and let our ideas play it back. Without warning, we will spin and lurch and then hold each other close. And when we stumble and run into each other and the beat is lost, we can stop, remind each other, and synchronise our steps again.

So too for the next thrust in meeting this challenge of AIDS.

As the epidemic moves through its second decade and the scale of the worldwide disaster mounts, our dreams must be big with strategies to match. Across all barriers, we must grasp every opportunity to build those 'true partnerships', to share risks and profits, to become associated players in the same game. We must become companions in dance.

Part 4

Derek Fraser's Songs

IN MEMORIAM DEREK ALLAN FRASER 22 October 1961 - 7 December 1994

I think continually of those who were truly great.
Who, from the womb, remembered the soul's history
Through corridors of light, where the hours are suns,
Endless and singing. Whose lovely ambition
Was that their lips, still touched with fire,
Should tell of the Spirit, clothed from head to foot in song.
And who hoarded from the Spring branches
The desires falling across their bodies like blossoms.

What is precious, is never to forget
The essential delight of the blood drawn from ageless springs
Breaking through rocks in worlds before our earth.
Never to deny its pleasure in the morning simple light
Nor its grave evening demand for love.
Never to allow gradually the traffic to smother
With noise and fog, the flowering of the spirit.

Near the snow, near the sun, in the highest fields,
See how these names are fêted by the waving grass
And by the streamers of white cloud
And whispers of wind in the listening sky.
The names of those who in their lives fought for life,
Who wore at their hearts the fire's centre.
Born of the sun, they travelled a short while toward the sun
And left the vivid air signed with their honour.

Sir Stephen Spender
The Truly Great

Chapter 31
A Light Where the Darkness Ends

History shows us that songs and struggle go hand in hand. When old comrades gathered in 1995 to mark the fiftieth anniversary of VE and VJ day, time and again it was songs which forged the link between present lives and shared struggles of the past.

It is now just ten years, not 50, since London Lighthouse began. Looking back over these years of our struggle in meeting the challenge of HIV/AIDS, sometimes heartbreaking, always rewarding, songs loom large. Musical photograph albums, songs evoke unremembered moments, anchoring faces and events in time and place. They recall familiar voices silenced by death, ripples of laughter grown faint with the passage of time. They revive tastes and textures and smells and sounds. They speak of triumphs and disasters, of loves and fights and dreams. They let loose forgotten feelings fenced in by the need to keep going at all costs, to jump the next hurdle, to meet the next challenge.

Sometimes, too, songs inspire us to look onwards and upwards. Just for a moment they light the way, beckoning us, reminding us that we can keep faith; or that we can stay with the struggle, whatever the struggle may be, taking risks, breaking new ground. Best of all perhaps, through songs we can touch again, however fleetingly, the essential truth that love changes everything.

This collection, Derek Fraser's Songs, originally published as a series of articles in *Lighthouse News* through the year following his death, is written in tribute to a remarkable young man, in his way a hero of this struggle. It is about Derek's life and work and death; and about some of the songs he chose for his funeral. These songs open a window onto something that mattered deeply to him, the vision of London Lighthouse.

In selecting Christmas carols and songs by Billie Holiday, Louis Armstrong, Frances Black and Jimmy Somerville, Derek made his funeral an occasion on which he spoke with eloquence and from his heart. The songs he chose are about life and love, justice and peace, empowerment and hope; about loss and death and the things of the spirit. All these are themes at the core of the Lighthouse vision.

In the days before the funeral, a friend of Derek's lovingly recorded cassettes of the music for friends to take away. On the cover of the cassette was the date, 15 December 1994, and the title, *Derek Fraser's Songs*. All year I have listened to that cassette, mostly on journeys, finding it a help in coming to terms with Derek's death and an inspiration in writing this tribute.

Every Friday London Lighthouse holds an open day. From all over the world a wide cross-section of visitors come to see the centre, to hear about the history and development of the project and about our model of care, and to ask a million questions about anything and everything connected with HIV and AIDS. As people arrive, taking their places in the Ian McKellen Hall and often, to their surprise, finding themselves intensely moved by the sheer beauty of the building and its atmosphere, as well as by the warmth of their welcome, we play a four-minute promotional video film, repeated over and over again.

Shot some years ago, the film shows Lighthouse in up-beat, celebratory mood one summer weekend when staff, including Derek Fraser, service users and supporters are setting up and hugely enjoying a fundraising lunch party. The soundtrack is Elton John's hit song 'Healing Hands', used with his permission, one of his many acts of generosity to Lighthouse over the years. As the camera zooms in on one smiling face after another, some of them clearly frail and who, like Derek, have since died, images and words are skilfully synchronised:

> *But giving into the nightmare ain't no cure for the pain*
> *You gotta wade into the water*
> *You gotta learn to live again.*

> *And reach out for her healing hands*
> *Reach out for her healing hands*
> *There's a light where the darkness ends.*

Wading into the water was Derek Fraser's way. Although only diagnosed HIV-positive later, he arrived to work at Lighthouse suspecting the truth. Drawn to the vision, with its hopeful flag hoist high, his disposition was always to grasp opportunity rather than to wallow in crisis. Without fuss he got on with the business of living and doing his job to the best of his ability.

And when the time came, that is the way he died.

Chapter 32
No Heart So True

I was first involved with AIDS when I became a buddy in 1986. My person with AIDS died 16 months later and I now have a genuine desire to work where gay people are helping with this problem. I believe I can maintain and improve standards of cleaning and security within the Lighthouse, improving the environment for residents, visitors and staff. I am friendly and outgoing, therefore my working relationships shall be an asset to the establishment.

So wrote Derek Fraser when first applying for a job at Lighthouse in 1989, just a few months after we had occupied our new building. What a priceless asset he turned out to be.

On a bleak December day five years later, in the Ian McKellen Hall, flowers in abundance, a single photograph of Derek on the wall behind the coffin, there was standing room only for his funeral. True to form, he had expressed clear wishes. His body was to be brought to our mortuary. He wanted to wear the kilt. Those who wished to see him could do so in the viewing room. The funeral was to take place at Lighthouse and there must be white heather on the coffin. The ceremony was to be built around his choice of songs and carols. This was to be a time for people to celebrate his life, to grieve and to say farewell.

Born in Fife, Scotland in 1961, Derek Allan Fraser was the youngest of seven children. His father, a retired miner, his mother and all his brothers and sisters made the journey to attend the funeral. Small in stature, Derek was lean, wiry, fierce, generous, energetic, industrious. Even now it is hard to think of him except in motion, rushing from one place to another, sweeping into a room and out again as soon as his mission was accomplished.

Good at his job as head of Building Services, Derek's purpose was to be real rather than liked. Never one to suffer fools gladly, he had a rough tongue. He lived life on his terms, spoke his mind on every issue and had no time whatever for pretence, or for beating about the bush.

But he was someone who inspired loyalty and affection on all sides especially from the staff in his group, paid and unpaid. As one of them said: 'Derek was fair, firm and funny'.

As a Scottish gay man from the working class, Derek was well aware of the reality of prejudice and oppression and of the political nature of AIDS. He could be a doughty fighter, fearlessly standing up for the rights of others, especially those whom he considered in any way disadvantaged or discriminated against, or who lacked a strong voice. Long before he was diagnosed HIV-positive himself, he championed the place in the project of people living with the virus, always making the needs of those using the services his first priority.

Never one to put himself in the limelight, Derek might have been surprised to find reflections on the Lighthouse vision dedicated to him. Of course, if they are to do him justice, they must be true to him - clear, honest, grounded. But anyone who knew him well also knew that he was passionate about Lighthouse, its philosophy and values. Woe betide anyone who ever tried to talk or do down the project. Yet he preferred to express his passion in deeds rather than words - that is until his funeral.

Derek refused to be victimised by his diagnosis and for many of us he was an inspiring example of empowerment. It is the straightforward, uncompromising, down-to-earth way he lived and worked and died, without apology or any shred of self-pity, that makes such a dedication appropriate. And at the end of his life, in his choice of songs for his funeral, at last he put words to what he felt so deeply about this central thread in the fabric of Lighthouse, its vision.

The approach of our landmark tenth anniversary year presented us with a good opportunity to think again about our vision and to bring the published statement up to date. This collection is some of my thoughts about the challenge of turning words on a page into action, on what it might mean to express this vision in every aspect of the life and work of Lighthouse.

As we gathered at the start of his funeral, we were greeted by Billie Holiday. Through the sadness it seemed to me that, on Derek's behalf, crooning throatily, she was embracing us:

> There is no greater love than what I feel for you,
> no greater love, no heart so true ...

Chapter 33
All the Time in the World

D erek Fraser was always in a rush, hastening from one task to the next. Given how reluctant he was to commit that most precious commodity of all, time, to reflective consideration of anything unless it served his first priority of getting the job done, one of the songs he chose for his funeral, at first glance, might come as a surprise.

> We have all the time in the world,
> Time enough for life to unfold
> all the precious things love has in store.
>
> We have all the love in the world.
> If that's all we have, you will find
> we need nothing more.
>
> Every step of the way will find us
> with the cares of the world far behind us.
>
> We have all the time in the world ...

What bearing could this song, so languorously sung by Louis Armstrong, have on our vision? What, anyway, do we mean by the word *vision* in the context of London Lighthouse? Why is a clearly-stated vision essential for the humanity, health and growth of an organisation such as this? What, when we examine it, is the content of this vision which meant so much to Derek Fraser, plain speaking, matter of fact and practical man that he was? What messages might there be in the songs he chose for his funeral?

What might be visible signs that Lighthouse lives up to its vision? What is it about organisations, true even of Lighthouse, that sometimes makes us lose sight of the values and aspirations which drew us in the first place? As any organisation matures, leaving behind the intensity and momentum of its earliest stirrings and, in our case at least, losing many of those who shaped it and many more since, how can its vision be kept bright, that is to say fresh, inspiring, motivating and relevant? In the marketplace of the contract culture where unit costs, monitoring mechanisms, efficiency and value for money are the currency of survival, what place is left for vision? Once an idea has taken institutional form, what possibilities may still beckon when enough people boldly commit to a shared vision and, as Goethe wrote, 'then providence moves too'?

As the AIDS pandemic unfolds, moving further ahead of the global response every year, and as Lighthouse approaches its tenth birthday, these are some of the questions we have been thinking about throughout the organisation. The product of this work, our revised vision statement, can be found in Appendix 3 at the end of the book.

'All that comes into view when the eyes are turned in the same direction' is one dictionary definition of the word vision. In the Old Testament, the Book of Proverbs is famously unequivocal: 'Where there is no vision, the people perish', an assertion of Fraserian abruptness. In fact, as Derek knew well, the Lighthouse vision is at once simple and profound. Its focus is a traditional mix of service provision and social change; yet in its totality, if we really turn our eyes towards it, it is disturbingly radical.

The Lighthouse vision statement has two parts, which we call aims and commitments. The aims summarise *what* we are trying to do, the commitments *how* we get there. Our aims are to provide high-quality care and support, empowering people with HIV and AIDS to live and die well; and to promote the changing of attitudes, leading to improved public policy and service provision. These are straightforward aims, providing services which make sense in human terms, coupled with influencing for change to create a social climate which fosters the most rational response to the epidemic.

These two aims are supported by four commitments. They concern, first, the centrality of people living with the virus in design and delivery of services and in running the organisation. Second, the creation of environments which offer an attentive welcome, matched by time and space for everyone, both those receiving and those providing services. Third, the recognition that death and dying are central to healthy living; that in a death-denying society the issues of death and loss need bringing into the open. Fourth, the challenging of oppression by speaking up for social justice, particularly for the human rights and civil liberties of all those living with and vulnerable to HIV.

London Lighthouse began with a few people in crisis deciding to support one another. Realising that in the face of a life-threatening diagnosis isolation might be as big an enemy as the virus itself, people spent time together in a particular way, making exciting discoveries along the way. They found that when listened to, well enough and long enough, they could think afresh; and that when listened to some more and asked incisive questions, those questions which take the thinker beyond the limiting assumptions of powerlessness, then they could put thinking into action, refuse to be victimised and often dramatically improve their lives.

Unwilling as he often seemed, even in the face of death, to stop and take time for himself, Derek Fraser understood and fiercely defended this guiding principle at the core of the Lighthouse vision. It is that this gift of time will, when given freely and with the loving, focused attention of one human being for another, even in the face of adversity and paradoxically even when time is short, most dependably lead us towards our power.

> *We have all the time in the world,*
> *Time enough for life to unfold*
> *all the precious things love has in store.*
>
> *Every step of the way will find us*
> *with the cares of the world far behind us.*
>
> *We have all the time in the world ...*

Chapter 34

As I Watch the Sun
Go Down

In my address at his funeral I paid tribute to the industry with which Derek Fraser promoted the project and its philosophy. This was often applied to the task of securing favourable terms from suppliers, or of soliciting donations and sponsorship. Sometimes it was put to use educating people whose business brought them into the centre, or, on occasion, defending Lighthouse from attack. In staff training he always helped people to see the relevance of the session to the Lighthouse vision. He loved Lighthouse and he had an irresistible way with people.

In due course Derek made his HIV status public, becoming a compelling communicator in the media. In just a few words he could convey the guts of what living with the virus was like for him in such a way that people could understand and respond. Once, in a television appearance when he talked about his strategies for maintaining equilibrium, there was a memorable moment. Without a flicker of fear or self-pity he looked straight at the interviewer, shrugged his shoulders and said, 'Yes, it's hard. Of course it's hard. After all, I'm going to die.' No mean task then, coming to terms with death. Yet, in spite of knowing his own death was beckoning and that there was bound to be suffering on the way, plainly Derek had arrived at a place of clarity, resolution and strength of purpose.

Derek and I became friends in the autumn of 1989 as a result of the death in an accident of a member of his staff in Building Services, Dayle Elkington. One day Dayle was at work, the next he was dead. Stunned, Derek and I found ourselves thrown together arranging for Dayle's body to be brought to our mortuary, planning his funeral and doing our best to support people at Lighthouse. Out of this tragedy there grew an enduring bond between us. On a late-night drive to the country to gather greenery for the funeral, we also started talking about death and dying, a conversation to which we would return from time to time until he died five years later.

Once the coroner had released Dayle's body, his coffin was brought to Lighthouse where it was carried through the front door and set down in reception. Many members of staff had gathered in welcome and flowers were laid on the coffin by Dayle's closest colleagues. With his return, reality could at last sink in and people begin to grieve, arms wrapped round one another for support. Even though we are accustomed to death at Lighthouse, I had never before seen the organisation intuitively dealing with a loss in such a public manner. I remember looking out beyond the circle of mourners and noticing that others were going about their business in the usual way, apparently unconcerned by the scene round Dayle's coffin. People were everywhere, coming to eat in the café, passing through to a training course, delivering packages at reception, arriving to call on residents.

At this moment I understood in a new way that part of our vision statement which affirms that death and dying are central to life and living, that these issues need bringing into the open. Here were life and death, side by side, in healthy balance. In this unscripted moment of greeting and grieving there was no hiding away, no pretence, no denial; and all around life was going on, business as usual.

In that diverse group there was a palpable sense of unity, of barriers between people dissolving, of our commitment to equality being *lived*, for a moment at least, spontaneously and with integrity. Lighthouse never felt safer, nor could I doubt that what was happening was profoundly healthy. It was a glimpse of what is possible, humanly speaking, when death is accorded its proper place, in the midst of life.

Supposing, I thought, such a scene was to take place, for example, in the town hall, or in a bank; supposing when an employee died it became customary for the coffin to be brought into the workplace so that colleagues could pay their respects and grieve together; and supposing this were to happen while people went about their business, paying their rent or cashing their cheques? Supposing we became a death-literate rather than death-denying society? How might this transform individuals, institutions, communities? How might it affect our capacity to contrive more rational, life-promoting solutions to the seemingly intractable problems besetting this troubled world?

At the end of Derek's funeral I was reminded of that incident round Dayle's coffin. With the utmost pathos and moving everyone to tears, Frances Black sung the ballad 'After the Ball', chosen because Derek's beloved grandmother used to sing it to him. Then we followed the coffin to the hearse waiting to take it to the crematorium. As we huddled together, united in sorrow, bracing ourselves to bid Derek final farewell, the December air was pierced by yet another voice.

This was Derek's compatriot, Jimmy Somerville, another proud gay man, with his searing, haunting lament, 'For A Friend':

> *And all the dreams we've had, I will carry on.*
> *As I watch the sun go down, watching the world fade away*
> *All the memories of you come rushing back to me.*
> *As I watch the sun go down, watching the world fade away*
> *All I want to do is kiss you once goodbye, goodbye.*
> *As I watch the sun go down, and darkness comes to me,*
> *All I want to do is kiss you once goodbye.*

So we said goodbye to Derek Allan Fraser, this bonny, brave man. He dared look death in the eye whilst living life to the full. And he was the staunchest of friends.

Chapter 35

Underneath the Mountain

Q*uestion*: What did Derek Fraser, Good King Wenceslas and the 1994 Paris Declaration have in common? *Answer:* A focus on the building of alliances to challenge oppression, to speak up for social justice, to promote human rights. Far fetched? Maybe, maybe not.

Perhaps surprisingly, Derek wanted a religious element in his funeral. But, since he was famously Christmas-crazy, it was no surprise that just before he died he decided on two carols. He did not say why he chose 'Good King Wenceslas': maybe it was just because it is up-beat and has a great tune; maybe it was for some other reason; we shall never know.

Born in 903, Wenceslas, Duke of Bohemia, tried to convert his people to Christianity. Then, aged only 33 - the same age as Derek - the poor Duke was murdered by his brother. Eventually he was canonised, becoming patron saint of Czechoslovakia.

The carol tells a rather inconclusive story. Wenceslas looks out of his window one snowy winter's evening and spots a man gathering firewood. 'Who is he and where does he live?', he asks his page. 'Oh, him,' replies the page - probably thinking, now what's coming? - 'he lives way across town, underneath the mountain, near St Agnes' Fountain ... a rough area, I'm afraid.'

'Never mind,' says the king, 'It's Boxing Day. We'll go round and make sure he gets a decent meal - fetch logs and meat and wine and let's get going.' The page is fed up - overtime without notice on a bank holiday, made to shoulder the victuals and the logs, and in this vile weather. So he has a bit of a moan - the dark, the cold, the distance, his feet, all this stuff to carry.

'Pull yourself together, stop whingeing and cheer up,' says the king, 'watch where I tread, follow me and walk faster - you'll soon warm up.' Obediently the page quickens his pace, finding to his astonishment that in the king's footsteps not only has the snow melted but the ground itself is quite warm.

Here, abruptly, the tale ends, except of course for the moral. If you are a Christian, whatever your station in life, bless the poor and you will find blessing. Missionary zeal? Seasonal, paternalistic whim expiating ruling-class guilt? Aware act of humanity, born of an alliance across the boundaries of oppression and of outrage at inequity and injustice? Like any of us, was Wenceslas just doing his best according to his lights?

On 1 December 1994, World AIDS Day, as Derek's life was ebbing away in the Middlesex Hospital, a big event was afoot in Paris, France. Heads or senior members of the governments of 42 countries, including the UK, representatives of the HIV/AIDS sector and people living with the virus were convening for a summit.

If we put cynicism about utterances by governments on hold, the Paris Declaration makes extraordinary, even hopeful reading. Mindful of the threat to humanity posed by the pandemic, it says, mindful of poverty and discrimination as factors in its spread and of its use as justification for grave violations of human rights; mindful of cultural, legal, economic and political obstacles hampering the response; mindful of the solidarity of community-based organisations and people living with HIV and AIDS ... Mindful of all this and more, it solemnly declares the obligation of signing countries to prioritise the fight against HIV/AIDS and against poverty, stigmatisation and discrimination, nationally and internationally.

It goes on to give numerous undertakings. These are that national policies will promote and protect the rights of those living with and vulnerable to HIV/AIDS; that people living with the virus, together with non-governmental organisations, will be involved in the formulation and implementation of public policy; that people living with HIV/AIDS will enjoy equal protection and access to services under the law; and that resources will be made available for prevention and care.

Finally it resolves to step up international co-operation through support for UNAIDS, the new global programme, for intersectoral partnerships and for the full participation of people living with HIV and AIDS in every aspect of the global response. Used wisely, as a tool not a weapon, by working collaboratively and by building on what is already in place, I believe this declaration provides the framework for which the world has been waiting. Our challenge now is to turn words into action.

Almost a year since Derek's death, December is here and soon we shall be singing carols again. All year we have mourned - we have reminisced and laughed and cried. His quilt, a work of love edged in

Fraser tartan, has occupied many hands, hearts and hours.

Sometimes, in my mind's eye, I see him about the place, scurrying through the café (where he hardly ever sat down) or at reception, arms folded, holding court with the fire brigade, summoned yet again by a false alarm. I hear his voice, hurling some ribald remark over his shoulder as he speeds by; admonishing someone for pulling a fast one or for forgetting what Lighthouse is here to do; or petitioning to right an injustice, fearlessly speaking up for those whose voice may not otherwise be heard.

The Paris Declaration maps the mountain of oppression, inequity, injustice and discrimination which underpins the pandemic, most of it in place long before AIDS arrived. But mountains have summits which can be scaled if climbers set their sights high and will rope themselves together.

Whatever Derek Fraser's religious beliefs, his aim was a fairer world, his method working with others to bring it about. Faithful in this as in every aspect of the Lighthouse vision, intrepid and resolute, he was a true mountaineer.

Part 5

Thro' the world we safely go

Joy and Woe are woven fine
A Clothing for the Soul divine
Under every grief and pine
Runs a joy with silken twine.

It is right it should be so
We were made for Joy and Woe;
And when this we rightly know
Thro' the World we safely go.

William Blake
From
Auguries of Innocence

Chapter 36
Many Happy Returns

The occasion for writing this book is the tenth anniversary of Lighthouse. Anniversaries can be bitter sweet. Benchmarks against which to measure achievement, they're also poignant reminders of all those precious people who are no longer part of the present picture, of just how much loss and change we've encountered on our way. Some of those people you've met in this book. Many more made their distinctive contribution to the story but have not made a personal appearance in these pages.

The loose-knit but intimate network of support from which Lighthouse grew has been replaced by a £5.5-million-a-year institution, wrapped around in all the paraphernalia of public reputation and accountability. Many of the pioneers who played their part in nurturing the dream of a place of safety and a beacon for change, and in making that dream come true, have now died. So birthdays at Lighthouse are moments for celebration and remembrance, both. They are also opportunities to assess how far we've stayed true to the dream. Ten years on, as we rightly take pride in what has been accomplished, we must also ponder again the extent to which the project is a worthy memorial to all those who have died.

On 5 August 1996 it will be ten years since we purchased the derelict Solomon Wolfson Jewish School in Lancaster Road, and London Lighthouse acquired legal entity as a registered charity and a non-profit-distributing company. A purpose-built centre would offer services aimed at meeting the particular needs of people affected by HIV and AIDS as defined by them, and its work would challenge the ignorance and prejudice underpinning a hostile social climate.

In spite of initial opposition and gloomy predictions that we had no idea what we were doing - well, we didn't, but we thought our way there - that the money would not be found and that the project would run out of steam, many thousands of people committed themselves to the challenge of turning an idea into reality. They cared passionately that we succeed.

Everyone who has been involved in seeing the project safely through these first ten years will agree that they've been years of struggle, risk, controversy, resourcefulness, intense public scrutiny, turbulence, change and a sometimes heartbreaking toll of loss and death. They will probably agree too that we couldn't possibly have imagined the gifts they would bring, nor the way our lives would change.

My friend Charles Maude, who died in August 1993, expressed it well. 'If someone was to offer to take this virus away, I couldn't refuse, the cost has been too high and too many people have died. But it is equally true that the benefits have been tremendous. In so many ways life has never been better and I wouldn't have missed a moment.'

In this book I have written about the challenges of building true partnerships, and of managing change, ambiguity and loss, as keys to long-range success. I have identified collaboration as the only workable device with which to secure lasting change. I have suggested that the transforming possibilities of this epidemic are most likely to be discovered when we hold in tension our commitment to excellence, together with willingness also to face the profoundly personal dimensions of the work.

If we can maintain the apparatus of institution in robust working order, working together to think our way to fresh solutions to old problems, solutions which are good for everyone, while at the same time keep comprehending the mystery of life and death in the context of AIDS, then we have nothing to fear. There will be no threat to the dream from the need to formalise, from political or funding vicissitudes, from the passage of time, nor from the incessant rollcall of death.

Lighthouse has organised as a hierarchy, clear about roles, responsibilities, lines of accountability and boundaries, as well as one strongly committed to equality. Woven into this structure with equal emphasis are some vital implicit rights; to maximum individual autonomy, to full discussion of every issue, and to high-quality personal support. Hierarchy with a human heart.

One-to-one supervision aims at an attentive environment in which workers can think well. A sensitive balance is struck between the professional and the personal, triumphs and disasters both opportunities to learn. A cycle of meetings within and between groups, including both workers and service users, sets out to elicit the best thinking of as many people as possible, from all levels and occupations, on every issue of note.

Meetings always include the opportunity for everyone present to speak personally as well as to contribute to the business in hand. A staff support system entitles everyone to one and a half hours of work time each week in a group of their choice. A highly-prized resource for those who use it, this fosters a climate which encourages people to be real about their experience, and to exchange intelligent informal support.

Symbolism plays a part in manifesting life at Lighthouse day by day. Those who have died are commemorated by a candle burning continuously in the quiet room, and by the fountain in the garden, a tree of life memorial to John Mordaunt who served on our Council until his death. Candles are lit on the reception desks on the ground and top floors for 24 hours marking the death of a resident, or of someone well-known to Lighthouse.

Coffins come and go in a respectful but routine way, part of the daily shifting scenery. As one component in a continuum of care, funerals take place most weeks at Lighthouse, allowing personal and collective farewells in ceremonials often planned by the person who has died. Annual conferences include a brief act of commemoration, a moment of recollection of those no longer with us, before embarking on the business of the day.

Our detractors, usually people with little direct experience of Lighthouse, sometimes accuse us of reinforcing an HIV=AIDS=death conspiracy, of glorifying death. People who use the services or who work in the project as paid and unpaid staff, and those who fall into both categories, know better. They say that healing, health and empowerment are possible when we don't have to pretend, when we can laugh and cry and fight as equals, when the environment champions everyone's capacity to think, and when the reality of death is clearly comprehended.

Learning to make flexible use of these disparate elements in our strategies for managing change, ambiguity and loss have I think been vital in our success, in balancing internal and external activity, and in the sheer amount that has been accomplished. So has the building of partnerships, an essential element in designing, executing and sustaining our strategies for change. Wherever opportunity knocks, locally, nationally and internationally, we try to work collaboratively. We see ourselves in partnership, with government, with health and local authorities, with other voluntary organisations in our sector and beyond, with the private sector, and with self-help and community groups of all kinds.

Between 1,500 and 2,000 people come into the centre each week for one purpose or another. Some come for structured services, counselling, complementary therapies, support groups, day or residential care; some for housing, welfare or legal advice; some to make use of the crèche or drop-in facilities, including the support and information service run so well by volunteers. Some come to participate in education or training activity, to attend an open day or to make commemorative quilts; some just to be with friends, to enjoy an entertainment, to use the café, the quiet room or the garden.

In our newly-acquired offices next door in Royalty Studios, the Community Services group manages the home support service, co-ordinating the activity of our 20 neighbourhood teams of volunteers, who provide practical and emotional support to more than 100 people living with the virus in their own homes across the city. Upstairs the Research and Policy group applies its skills to the task of internal audit and supporting our influencing for change work, scrutinising relevant data and considering how and where this information needs feeding into organisational or public policy.

A brisk ten-minute walk away at Latimer Lighthouse, the Education and Management Services division combines the tasks of communicating the Lighthouse approach far and wide through training and consultancy, with providing the support services necessary to keep an operation of this scale afloat. Finance and Information Systems manages our money and technology; Personnel takes care of recruitment, employee relations, staff support and of drafting organisational policy. Communications handles our relations with the media, the distribution of information and publications. Building Services maintains the buildings and keeps the gardens beautiful. Here the Funding group, in addition to bringing in the revenue for this year's budget, is working on the tenth anniversary capital appeal.

This appeal for £1.5 million is to extend our main building onto some land we've bought at the rear of the main site. The additional space will be largely dedicated to developing services for the increasing numbers of children and families needing Lighthouse, as well as to adding to the number of single rooms for residents and providing improved space for the delivery of medical care and complementary therapies.

In coming to the end of this book, I am especially conscious of all those without whom London Lighthouse would not exist. In addition to the many who have died, I think particularly of those living with HIV and AIDS from whom the project derives so much authority, integrity and vigour.

I salute a magnificent workforce, paid and unpaid, full and part time, past and present, whose buoyancy, humour and strength has daily made miracles. I appreciate colleagues in the sector, some of whom I have known well for ten years, who take such care to see that our work dovetails. I am daily grateful to our many funders who continue to trust enough to finance the work.

I am thankful for those countless supporters across the country and beyond these shores who watch, hold us in their hearts and signal their solidarity in countless ways. In wishing Lighthouse happy birthday, and pledging it to keep up its good work while HIV/AIDS is with us, I wish you, the reader, whoever and wherever you may be, many happy returns too. Many happy returns to you to the Lighthouse, where a warm welcome always awaits you. I thank you all for the part you play and ask you to keep on sustaining us as we face whatever challenges our second decade may bring.

Come, come,
Whoever you are,
Wanderer, worshipper, lover of learning,
It doesn't matter.
Ours is not a caravan of despair.
Come, even if you've broken your vow a thousand times.
Come, come, yet again, come.

Chapter 37
Flowers in a Vase

It has taken me just three weeks to complete this arrangement. Balmy, early autumn days; misty mornings giving way truculently to clear blue skies and watery sunshine; dark descending abruptly on still summer-mild nights. My buckets, in reality Lighthouse blue box files, are empty, their contents worked into the text or discarded clippings.

Glorious, exhilarating weeks spent in virtual seclusion in Oxfordshire. Weeks of indistinguishable days, rising very early, savouring the secret pleasure of hours when others sleep, watching dawn break through my study window, my head bursting with ideas crowding in overnight.

All the words that I utter,
And all the words that I write,
Must spread out their wings untiring,
And never rest in their flight,
Till they come where your sad, sad heart is,
And sing to you in the night,
Beyond where the waters are moving,
Storm-darken'd or starry bright.

Three weeks of writing, writing, writing, absorbed and totally focused, just as when I'm arranging flowers. A wonderful, rare chance to luxuriate in what one friend terms the 'tunnel vision' of the writer at work.

I say virtual seclusion because there have been two important intrusions. First a visit from my siblings midway between the anniversaries of our parents' deaths, one and two years ago respectively. They didn't live to read this book, but of course it's full of them, as is this house where they lived in their last years.

They championed the Lighthouse unconditionally, happily taking my work and circle into their hearts and into this house. Without hesitation they took AIDS in their stride and expected everyone they knew to do so too. Each made it to see the completed Lighthouse just once, everything to me.

My mother's nursing home organised a coach outing, bringing her and 30 other frail, confused residents to tea in the Lighthouse café one Christmas. 'And where are the *patients*?', she asked from her wheelchair, imperious, ever the St Thomas's Hospital ward sister. It turned into a great party, with carol singing led by a cabaret singer volunteer who happened to be on duty, buttonholes and small presents conjured up by another on the spur of the moment.

My mother was queen bee, demanding a complete tour of inspection. She was someone, it was said at her funeral, 'always drawn to spending her time in ways that made a real difference in people's lives'. Unfailingly generous, she rejoiced in the Lighthouse. As well as a love of flowers, more than anyone it was she who taught me that if you want peace, you must work for justice.

My father dispensed much armchair wisdom of the 'Of course, it's well known that cats have no sense of time' variety. Still, he believed in the project and he believed in me. At other times in my life I could never have imagined that such amity would one day exist between us. But never for a moment did I doubt him on writing. Good writing was his passion, a gift he passed on to his children as lifeblood.

And I loved the time we had here together towards the end. He would sit in his winged armchair in the corner of 'the long room', beside the spot where the green pedestal with flowers now stands, surrounded by small tables piled high with his beloved books, wearing several pairs of spectacles and holding up whatever he was reading - poetry, biography, military history, Trollope, the Psalms - to catch the light.

From one of his favourite anthologies we took lines for his funeral:

> This is the end
> Foretold and dreamed -
> 'Colour and light and all warm lovely things'.
> The last, Earth's last horizon eyes transcend
> The mirage.
> Homeward, warrior poet the evening brings.

They asked that there be no grave and that instead we scatter their ashes in the Thames where they loved to row their boat in the evenings. So after two funerals and two ashes-scattering ceremonies in little more than a year, this family get-together was to dedicate a simple plaque which we've put up in the garden in their memory. Engraved glass mounted on grey Lakeland slate, it glints brightly when it catches the sun. Andrew Henderson, always in my parent's minds a much-loved honorary son, composed a prayer for the occasion, giving thanks 'for the hospitality and fun we enjoyed here with them; for their pleasure in this house, the river and the garden'.

I arranged a mass of my mother's favourite shell-pink lilies, *Lilium japonicum*, in an opaque jade-green glass vase she loved. Those lilies have since grown daily shade-by-shade paler, now the tint of pink champagne. On the dining table, in contrast, in my father's 1909 silver christening bowl, I arranged a cacophony of garden colour. Self-seeded *Nerine bowdenii*, candy-floss pink. Coreopsis *American dream*, brilliant vermilion, small ragged-bloomed chrysanthemum, bronze *Brightness* and pale gold *Mary Stoker*, aster *frikartii*, lavender-blue with bright yellow eyes, late penstemon and creamy freesia (from the market), ruby red *Dublin Bay* rose, all well-scented with a froth of silver *Artemnesia arborescens*. We ate family favourites, coq au vin and treacle tart, the recipe with fresh cream, grated apple, lemon juice and ground ginger. Accustomed now to our orphan state, it was an easy, convivial time, my only day off.

The second intrusion concerns cats, most important players in my story. Over the years I've inherited numerous cats from people living with HIV/AIDS, seven the most at any one time (which Nancy thinks is two too many).

Graham Gardner's first blow against his isolation was to acquire two cats. Sid, a handsome, uncomplicated tabby, a born organiser with extensive social commitments in the neighbourhood, and Bella, an exquisite coffee and cream Burman who lives life on a knife-edge of emergency, never daring to venture beyond dashing distance of the cat door. Graham quickly progressed from cats to people and the cats came to live with me.

Soon they were joined by Panther, a big black-deep-chocolate-brown part-Persian with a torn ear and a bushy tail. We heard that a man with AIDS was dying in Walton-on-Thames, distressed because no arrangements were in place for his beloved cat. One evening John Shine and I drove down there, finding both the man and the cat in a sorry state. At the man's insistence, I agreed to bring Panther home with me.

He was a fighter, clearly disliking both people and other cats, spending his time out of sight and reach on top of the kitchen cupboards, apparently coming down to eat, though never with anyone there to witness it. He was an enormous challenge, requiring hours and hours of patient counselling. But the effort paid off and presently he emerged, the tenderest, gentlest, most affectionate and communicative cat you can imagine. Now he likes to sleep in the crook of my arm for as long as I can stand not to disturb either him or Nancy by turning over in bed.

The cats moved with me to Oxfordshire, taking to country life, and Nancy, in due course, taking to them. Other cats have come and gone and now we're left with just these three. Liking the idea of giving a home to more unwanted adult cats, rather than rearing kittens, we got in touch with the Cats Protection League. So one late afternoon's writing was interrupted by local CPL officials coming to inspect us as prospective adopters, bringing enticing coloured photographs of cats looking for new owners. They pronounced the place 'a paradise for cats' and we passed muster. Carlton and Corbin, ginger and white two-year-old brothers, are the entirely delicious result.

The pattern of my days has been very ordered. Seven or eight hours writing followed by a peanut butter, honey and banana sandwich and a long walk. Then a few more hours writing until the evening. This is when I meet Nancy, hard at work on her first novel at the other end of the house. Over tortillas and a drink, we read each other everything we've written that day, then eat supper and go early to bed.

Invariably my walks have been in one of three favourite spots. I walk by the river at Clifton Hampden, along the bank opposite Christopher Gibbs' house, where Andrew and I solicited the support of the John Paul Getty Junior Charitable Trust almost ten years ago. Here I always pass a scattering of men fishing with undistractable concentration. Or I go to Wittenham Clumps, our local 'twin peaks', a landmark for miles around, walking down through the fields to the lock at Little Wittenham, where the lock keeper sells second-hand paperbacks and pooh-sticks for 1p each.

Or, best of all, I risk the car's undercarriage by going to the very top of Cholsey Downs and walking along the famous Ridgeway Path towards the Lambourn Downs, crossing the county line into Berkshire. For a valley dweller like me this is the top of the world. Pulled into the present by the wide open sky and so much beauty, I'm transported by the view north-west across the Vale of the White Horse, north-east over the Vale of Aylesbury and due south towards Newbury. With luck I meet only pheasants, a lone hiker or two, or perhaps some children out hacking on their ponies along the way.

The harvest is safely gathered in, fields ploughed and resown with winter wheat. Hawthorn berries are turning the darkest blood red. Nervy birch flusters in the wind, silver bark peeling, leaves marbled green to gold and every shade between. The willows shimmer on, silver-grey-green river sentries, not yet nodding to autumn. Surprisingly, the beeches still look green, till I walk underneath their swooping branches treading a carpet of bronze leaves and tiny brown nuts popped from split, spiky husks. Disappointed blackberries wither on the bush, too late to ripen now. Straggling wisps of rosebay willow-herb, all colour gone, hang like tired flags flown too long. Old man's beard romps ecstatically through the hedgerows; ivy flowers thick, bulbous and defiant, unafraid of winter lying in wait.

Up here, almost as far from the sea and any lighthouse as it's possible to get, I don't really think about this book. Instead I suppose I touch the 'dearest freshness, deep down things', in the quiet suddenly noticing I'm breathing clean, warm air, that I'm alive and strong. Up here, in thrall to the beauty, I feel free. As I look into the distance I know I am close to myself, safe, connected to the Lighthouse, bound to this work by choice, my writing a joyous act of purification.

I remember lines from 'The Celtic Twilight' by W B Yeats, framed in my office, the gift of an Irish friend, read and reread a thousand times over the years:

We can make our minds so like still water
that beings gather about us that they may see,
it may be, their own images,
and so live for a moment with a clearer,
perhaps even with a fiercer life because of our quiet.

Appendix 1
The UK Declaration of Rights of People with HIV and AIDS

Preface: This Declaration is made by people with HIV and AIDS and by organisations dedicated to their welfare. The Declaration lists rights which all citizens of the United Kingdom, including people with HIV and AIDS, enjoy under international law; the Declaration then prescribes measures and recommends practices which the writers of the Declaration believe are the minimum necessary to ensure that these rights are respected and protected within the United Kingdom.

The Declaration: All citizens of the United Kingdom, including people with HIV and AIDS, are accorded the following rights under international law: the right to liberty and security of person; the right to privacy; the right to freedom of movement; the right to work; the right to housing, food, social security, medical assistance and welfare; the right to freedom from inhumane or degrading treatment; the right to equal protection of the law and protection from discrimination; the right to marry; the right to found a family; the right to education.

These rights exist in international treaties (1) which the United Kingdom Government has agreed to uphold. But these rights, as they apply to United Kingdom citizens with HIV and AIDS, have not been adequately respected or protected. We therefore make a public Declaration of the Rights of People with HIV and AIDS and of our commitment to ensuring that they are upheld.

Liberty and Security: People with HIV and AIDS have the right to liberty and security of person, and in respect of this right we believe that: 1. No person should be subjected to forcible detention, isolation, or segregation from society purely on the grounds of their having HIV, or having AIDS or an AIDS-related condition; 2. No prisoner should be segregated from other prisoners purely on the grounds of their having HIV, or having AIDS or an AIDS-related condition. We affirm and hold, in agreement with the World

Health Organisation, that 'persons suspected or known to be HIV-infected should remain integrated with society ...' (2)

Privacy: People with HIV and AIDS have the right to privacy, and in respect of this right, we believe that: 3. Information about the HIV status of any person should be kept confidential to that person and their appointed health and social carers (except where anonymous information is given to a public body for the purpose of studying the epidemiology of HIV); 4. Information should not be disclosed to a third party about a person's HIV status without that person's consent; 5. In accordance with a judgement of the European Court of Human Rights, the right to privacy includes the right 'to establish and develop relationships with other human beings, especially in the emotional sphere, for the development and fulfilment of one's own personality.' (3)

Freedom of Movement: People with HIV and AIDS have the right to freedom of movement, and in respect of this right we believe that: 6. No restrictions should be placed on the free movement of individuals within and between States purely on the grounds of their having HIV, or having AIDS or an AIDS-related condition. We affirm and hold, in agreement with the Committee of Ministers of the Council of Europe, that 'in the light of present knowledge, discriminatory measures such as control at borders ... should not be introduced as they are not justified either scientifically or ethically.' (4)

Work: People with HIV and AIDS have the right to work, and in respect of this right we believe that: 7. No person should be barred from employment or dismissed from employment purely on the grounds of their having HIV, or having AIDS or an AIDS-related condition; 8. Employers should ensure that their terms and conditions of employment are such as to enable people with HIV, AIDS or an AIDS-related condition to continue in their employment, and to do so in a healthy and safe working environment; 9. Employers or their agents should not perform tests to detect the HIV status of current or prospective employees; 10. In respect of the right to work, the right to privacy and the right to protection from discrimination, there should be no obligation or requirement upon an individual to disclose to an employer their own HIV status, or the HIV status of another person.

Housing, Food, Social Security, Medical Assistance and Welfare: All persons, including those with HIV and AIDS, have the right to housing, food, social security, medical assistance and welfare.

In respect of the right to housing, food and social security, we note that

Article 11 of the International Covenant on Economic, Social and Cultural Rights states: 'The states parties to the present covenant recognise the right of everyone to an adequate standard of living for himself and his family, including adequate food, clothing and housing ...'

In respect of these rights, we believe that individuals with HIV and AIDS, and their dependants, who are in social or housing need should be offered: 11. The prompt provision of housing which is beneficial to their physical and mental well-being; 12. The provision of adequate means, through direct financial assistance and provision by appropriate social care agencies, to maintain a reasonable standard of living and especially an appropriate diet.

In respect of the right to medical assistance and welfare, we believe that people with HIV, AIDS or an AIDS-related condition should have: 13. Full access to available medical treatment, including complementary and experimental therapies, without charge to the recipient; 14. Access to blood products of the highest quality, for those dependent on them; 15. Free access to a data-base providing information about therapeutic research in relation to HIV infection, AIDS and associated conditions; 16. Access to provision by statutory and voluntary agencies of social care by appropriately trained workers; 17. For those who have problems with illegal substances, access to a full range of services (including maintenance therapy) that is appropriate to their needs; 18. Care unprejudiced by the agreement or refusal to participate in research trials.

In relation to social and medical care, we believe that people with HIV and AIDS should: 19. Be fully involved in a working partnership with medical, health and social care workers and researchers to develop policies and practices which meet their medical, health and social care needs.

In relation to medical care we believe that people with HIV and AIDS should: 20. Be able to refuse treatment or restrict their treatment to palliative care.

In respect of the right to medical assistance, and of the duty of Governments to protect the health of citizens, we urge the United Kingdom Government to allocate a proper proportion of available resources towards therapeutic research into HIV infection and conditions associated with AIDS.

Equal Protection of the Law and Protection from Discrimination: People with HIV and AIDS have the right to equal protection of the law and protection from discrimination. We note the statement of the World Health Organisation that: 'The avoidance of discrimination against persons known or suspected to be HIV-infected is important for AIDS prevention and control: failure to prevent such discrimination may endanger public health.' (5)

In respect of the right to protection from discrimination we believe that: 21. Measures should be taken to protect people with HIV and AIDS from discrimination in the areas of employment, housing, education, faith, legal services, child care and the provision of medical, social and welfare services, and from arbitrary and commercially unjustified discrimination by private insurance companies; 22. There should be other appropriate provision to protect people with HIV and AIDS, and their dependants, from social disadvantage arising from commercially justified discrimination by private insurance companies.

We note that the World Summit of Ministers of Health on Programmes for AIDS Prevention (hosted by the UK Government) emphasised in the London Declaration on AIDS Prevention (1988) 'the need in AIDS prevention programmes to protect human rights and human dignity' and undertook to 'forge, through information and education and social leadership, a spirit of social tolerance'. In pursuit of this, we believe that: 23. There should be public education whose specific objective is the elimination of discrimination against people with HIV and AIDS.

In support of the above we note that Article 26 of the International Covenant on Civil and Political Rights (which is binding on the United Kingdom Government) states: 'All persons are equal before the law and are entitled without any discrimination to the equal protection of the law. In this respect the law shall prohibit any discrimination and guarantee to all persons equal and effective protection against discrimination on any ground such as race, colour, sex, language, religion, political or other opinion, national or social origin, property, birth or other status.' We submit that HIV status and HIV-related disability fall within the 'other status' covered by this prohibition of discrimination.

To Marry and to found a Family: People with HIV and AIDS have the right to marry and the right to found a family, and in respect of these rights we believe that: 24. Full and appropriate counselling and information, which respects their right to parent children, and the right of women with HIV to bear children, should be available to those people with HIV and AIDS who wish to exercise this right. (6)

Education: People with HIV and AIDS have the right to education, and in respect of this right: 25. Education should not be impaired by restrictions on social interaction placed on people with HIV and AIDS in educational settings.

We believe these measures are necessary to ensure that the rights of people with HIV and AIDS, and of others disadvantaged as a result of disability or medical condition, are protected in a society which respects the value and dignity of its members.

Notes: (1) The relevant treaties, which the UK Government has agreed to uphold, are: the International Covenant on Civil and Political Rights; the International Covenant on Economic, Social and Cultural Rights (1976); the European Convention on Human Rights (1953); the European Social Charter (1965). (2) Social Aspects of AIDS Prevention and Control Programmes (World Health Organisation, Geneva, 1987). (3) Dudgeon v United Kingdom, Judgement of the European Court of Human Rights (1981) 4 EHRR 149. (4) Appendix to Recommendation No. R (87) 25, para 2.2.2. (5) Social Aspects of AIDS Prevention and Control Programmes (World Health Organisation, Geneva, 1987). (6) Where a woman with HIV or AIDS chooses to have a child, it should be the right of both the woman and the child that the mother be given full support and that all possible procedures be adopted to minimise the risk of HIV transmission from mother to child, before, during and after birth.

This Declaration was produced by a working group of representatives from: AIDS and Housing Project; Black HIV and AIDS Network; Blackliners; Body Positive; Broadcasting Support Services; Frontliners UK; The Haemophilia Society; The Landmark; London Lighthouse; NAHAW (National Association of HIV and AIDS Workers); National AIDS Manual; National AIDS Trust; NOVOAH (Network of Voluntary Organisations AIDS/HIV); Positively Women; SCODA (Standing Conference on Drug Abuse); Scottish AIDS Monitor; Terrence Higgins Trust.

Appendix 2
The Paris Declaration

We, the Heads of Government or Representatives of the 42 states*
assembled here in Paris 1 December 1994:

I. Mindful that the AIDS pandemic, by virtue of its magnitude, constitutes a
threat to humanity; that its spread is affecting all societies; that it is hindering
social and economic development, in particular of the worst affected
countries, and increasing disparities within and between countries; that
poverty and discrimination are contributing factors in the spread of the
pandemic; that HIV/AIDS inflicts irreparable damage on families and
communities; that the pandemic concerns all people without distinction but
that women, children and youth are becoming infected at an increasing rate,
that not only causes physical and emotional suffering but is often used as the
justification for grave violations of human rights,

Mindful also that obstacles of all kinds - cultural, legal, economic and political
- are hampering information, prevention, care and support efforts; that
HIV/AIDS prevention and care and support strategies are inseparable, and
hence must be an integral component of an effective and comprehensive
approach to combating the pandemic; that new local, national and
international forms of solidarity are emerging, involving in particular people
living with HIV/AIDS and community-based organisations,

II. Solemnly declare our obligation as political leaders to make the fight
against HIV/AIDS a priority; our obligation to act with compassion for and in
solidarity with those with HIV or at risk of becoming infected, both within our
societies and internationally; our determination to ensure that all persons
living with HIV/AIDS are able to realise the full and equal enjoyment of their
fundamental rights and freedoms without distinction and under all
circumstances; our determination to fight against poverty, stigmatisation and

discrimination; our determination to mobilise all of society - the public and private sectors, community-based organisations and people living with HIV/AIDS - in a spirit of true partnership; our appreciation and support for the activities and work carried out by the multilateral, intergovernmental, non-governmental and community-based organisations, and our recognition of their important role in combating the pandemic; our conviction that only more vigorous and better coordinated action worldwide, sustained over the long term - such as that to be undertaken by the joint and co-sponsored United Nations programme on HIV/AIDS - can halt the pandemic,

III. Undertake in our national policies to protect and promote the rights of individuals, in particular those living with or most vulnerable to HIV/AIDS, through the legal and social environment; fully involve non-governmental and community-based organisations as well as people living with HIV/AIDS in the formulation and implementation of public policies; ensure equal protection under the law for persons living with HIV/AIDS with regard to access to health care, employment, education, travel, housing and social welfare; intensify the following range of essential approaches for the prevention of HIV/AIDS:

1. Support a greater involvement of people living with HIV/AIDS through an initiative to strengthen the capacity and co-ordination of networks of people living with HIV/AIDS and community-based organisations. By ensuring their full involvement in our common response to the pandemic at all - national, regional and global - levels, this initiative will, in particular, stimulate the creation of supportive political, legal and social environments; 2. Promote global collaboration for HIV/AIDS research by supporting national and international partnerships between the public and private sectors, in order to accelerate the development of prevention and treatment technologies, including vaccines and microbicides, and to provide for the measures needed to help ensure their accessibility in developing countries. This collaborative effort should include related social and behavioural research; 3. Strengthen international collaboration for blood safety with a view to coordinating technical information, proposing standards for good manufacturing practices for all blood products, and fostering the establishment and implementation of cooperative partnerships to ensure blood safety in all countries.

We urge all countries and the international community to provide the resources necessary for the measures and initiatives mentioned above. We call upon all countries, the future joint and co-sponsored United Nations programme on HIV/AIDS and its six member organisations and programmes to take all steps possible to implement this Declaration in coordination with multilateral and bilateral aid programmes and intergovernmental and non-governmental organisations.

Paris, 1 December 1994

*Argentina; Australia; Bahamas; Belgium; Brazil; Burundi; Cambodia; Cameroon; Canada; China; Côte d'Ivoire; Denmark; Djibouti; Finland; France; Germany; India; Indonesia; Italy; Japan; Mexico; Morocco; Mozambique; Netherlands; Norway; Philippines; Portugal; Romania; Russian Federation; Senegal; Spain; Sweden; Switzerland; Thailand; Tunisia; Uganda; United Kingdom of Great Britain and Northern Ireland; United Republic of Tanzania; United States of America; Vietnam; Zambia; Zimbabwe.

Appendix 3
The London Lighthouse Vision Statement

London Lighthouse was set up to tackle the challenges faced by people affected by HIV and AIDS.

The project has two main aims:

- To provide high-quality care and support, in centres and in people's homes, to empower people with HIV and AIDS to live and die well.

- To promote the changing of attitudes to HIV and AIDS and to help make sure good public policies and services for affected people are developed.

These aims are supported by four commitments:

- To make sure that people living with HIV and AIDS are central in the organisation, so they can influence policies, develop services and actively contribute to the decision-making process.

- To create safe and welcoming environments which offer time and space to meet the needs of service users, carers, paid and unpaid staff and visitors.

- To challenge the denial of death - to bring the issue of death into the open and recognise that it is part of life and living.

- To challenge oppression, discrimination and prejudice, promote equal opportunities and to speak up for social justice.

Notes on Sources

The sources not given in the text for quotations are as follows. Some material in chapter 23, 'London-wide', is drawn from 'Collaboration of Service NGOs in a Market Environment', paper delivered at the Second BioPsychoSocial Aspects of AIDS conference, Brighton, England, 8 July 1994 by Lisa Power (written by Lisa Power and Christopher Spence). The verse in chapter 27, 'Wise Before His Time', is from 'Through the Night of Doubt and Sorrow' by B S Ingemann (1786-1862), translator Sabine Baring Gould (1834-1924), in the *English Hymnal* (Oxford University Press). In chapter 36, 'Many Happy Returns', the verse 'Come, come' is from *The Masnavi* of Jellaludin Rumi (1207-1273). The quotation in chapter 37, 'Flowers in a Vase', is an extract from W B Yeats, 'Where My Books Go', included in *The Oxford Book of English Verse 1250-1900* (reproduced by kind permission of A P Watt Ltd on behalf of Anne and Michael Yeats).

Index

All the author's royalties from the sale of this book will be given to the Lighthouse to support the building of collaborative partnerships with non-governmental organisations (NGOs) working in response to HIV/AIDS in the developing world.